Principled Leadership
in MENTAL HEALTH SYSTEMS AND PROGRAMS

Boston University Center for Psychiatric Rehabilitation

12-12-08

Dear Ken,

It was great to meet you at the N.C. training on preventing violence, & Thanks for buying This book!

Best of luck in the future

Sincerely
Kevin Huckshorn

Principled Leadership
in MENTAL HEALTH SYSTEMS AND PROGRAMS

William A. Anthony and Kevin Ann Huckshorn

Published by:

Center for Psychiatric Rehabilitation
Boston University
940 Commonwealth Avenue West
Boston, MA 02215
http://www.bu.edu/cpr/

The Center for Psychiatric Rehabilitation is partially funded by the National
Institute on Disability and Rehabilitation Research and the Center for Mental
Health Services, Substance Abuse and Mental Health Services Administration.

Printed in the United States of America

Library of Congress Control Number: 2008921275
ISBN13: 978-1-878512-22-2
ISBN10: 1-878512-22-6

*To all the people who have helped make the
vision of recovery from severe mental illnesses a reality.*

*The publication of this book was supported in part by
The Elizabeth Whitney Post Fund, Sargent College of Health and
Rehabilitation Sciences, Boston University.*

*All proceeds from the sale of this text are used to further the work of
the Center for Psychiatric Rehabilitation. No royalties are paid to the authors.*

CONTENTS

ABOUT THE AUTHORS

William A. Anthony, PhD, is executive director of Boston University's Center for Psychiatric Rehabilitation and a professor in the University's College of Health and Rehabilitation Sciences.

For the past 35 years, Anthony has worked in various roles in the field of mental health and psychiatric rehabilitation, and has been honored for his performance as a researcher, an educator, and a clinician. He is currently co-editor of the *Psychiatric Rehabilitation Journal.*

In 1988, Anthony received the Distinguished Services Award from the National Alliance on Mental Illness in recognition of "his efforts that challenge outdated ideas which limit the potential of mentally ill people. The innovative programs created through Bill Anthony's leadership offer hope and opportunity." Anthony has appeared on ABC's "Nightline," which featured a rehabilitation program developed and implemented by Boston University's Center for Psychiatric Rehabilitation. Ted Koppel characterized it as a model program: "a small beacon of sanity in dealing with the problems of those whose sanity has crumbled."

In 1992, Anthony received the Distinguished Service Award from the President of the United States for his efforts "promoting the dignity, equality, independence, and employment of people with disabilities."

Anthony has authored over 100 articles in professional journals, 14 textbooks, and several dozen book chapters. A few of Anthony's latest professional books are: *Psychiatric Rehabilitation Programs: Putting Theory into Practice* (co-edited with Dr. Marianne Farkas), *Psychiatric Rehabilitation* (authored with Dr. Mikal Cohen, Dr. Marianne Farkas, and Dr. Cheryl Gagne), *Readings in Psychiatric Rehabilitation* (co-edited with Dr. LeRoy Spaniol), and *Toward a Vision of Recovery.*

Kevin Ann Huckshorn, RN, MSN, CAP, ICDC, is director of the Office of Technical Assistance for the National Association for State Mental Health Program Directors (NASMHPD) and the National Coordinating Center for Seclusion and Restraint Reduction.

Ms. Huckshorn is a licensed and certified mental health nurse and substance abuse clinician with practical knowledge from 25 years of professional frontline experience working in a variety of public and private mental health organizations and substance abuse programs. She has extensive experience in both inpatient and outpatient program development including peer-run projects, psychiatric rehabilitation treatment programs for persons with serious mental illness, and recovery-based mental health and substance abuse services. In her current role, she manages multiple technical assistance projects, organizes state and national meetings, and monitors all services and products—from action plans to pragmatic tools and training for applying promising and evidence-based practices.

Ms. Huckshorn is a frequent speaker at national conferences related to behavior health and also works internationally on such issues as the prevention of violence and the use of seclusion and restraint in mental health settings. She is currently in the dissertation phase of her doctoral program; has published articles on violence, treatment adherence, and workforce development; and serves on the editorial boards of three U.S. peer-reviewed mental health journals.

FOREWORD

Many books have been written about leadership, but few, if any, have addressed leadership in the world of mental health services. Historically, books on leadership have fallen primarily into three categories: those written by academics who have researched the topic, those written by consultants who make a living advising corporate executives on leadership, and those written by successful executives who tell their own story and articulate the principles of leadership that they created or followed. Unlike business leadership books that focus on sustainable competitive advantage, topline growth, and/or improved profitability, *Principled Leadership* has human satisfaction and success as its outcome metric. For the authors, as well as the leaders who were interviewed for *Principled Leadership,* the desired outcome of an effective mental health organization is *people who can live, learn, and work in the environments of their choice.*

Anthony and Huckshorn have studied leadership, advised leaders in the field of mental health, and have been leaders themselves in transforming services for people who experience mental illnesses. Each has played a critical role in shaping a mental health movement—psychiatric rehabilitation and seclusion/restraint reduction, respectively—and each has extensive leadership experiences in mental health that are value based, outcome focused, and recovery oriented. Yet this book is not about Anthony and Huckshorn's leadership activities. In line with the leadership principle advanced in chapter 8, which is to build organizations around exemplars, Anthony and Huckshorn have organized this book around exemplary leaders who model principled leadership.

The vision, values, principles, and tasks discussed by these leaders go beyond any one specific approach to solving the difficult problems faced by the people affected by serious mental illnesses and their families who support them. Effective leadership, as described in this book, is based on understanding the possibilities of transformation, rather than predicting and controlling probabilities. Most of all, *Principled Leadership* offers leaders, and would-be leaders, a vision that goes beyond methods and approaches that can be divisive and exclusive. It describes mental health systems and programs that are driven by the unifying constructs of recovery, hope, and choice, and it articulates the principles and tasks that are critical for effective leadership of these organizations.

Anthony and Huckshorn convince us that principled leadership in mental health is necessary and possible—and that principled leaders can make a difference in the lives of people and in our society. They convince us that principled leaders can be developed, and they provide a blueprint for doing so. Further, they argue that a critical mass of principled leaders can transform our mental health system—and that it is our responsibility to build that critical mass of principled leaders.

I congratulate the authors on this breakthrough book, which I believe will be a landmark in the leadership literature. Like *Principled Leadership*, business leadership books stress the importance of outcomes—but profit and market share outcomes are not focused singularly on helping people, families, and communities to become more successful and satisfied. Unfortunately, too often the goals of our business leaders create the conditions for human suffering, rather than human success and satisfaction. *Principled Leadership* is an invaluable text for leaders and future leaders in the mental health field—and the basic principles and tasks articulated in *Principled Leadership* are relevant for all business leaders.

BARRY F. COHEN
EXECUTIVE VICE PRESIDENT
PARAMETRIC TECHNOLOGY CORPORATION

PREFACE

In our respective travels, nationally and internationally, we have been intrigued with the drastic differences in how mental health organizations innovate and change. Some organizations (centers, hospitals, programs, units, etc.) embrace the opportunity to improve. Others are much less enthusiastic about the possibility of improvement and seem to impede or ignore their prospects for continued progress. We attribute much of these organizational differences to leadership, and it is that strong belief that led to this book.

In the United States, during the latter part of the 20th century and the beginning of the 21st century, the need for transformational change in the mental health system has been magnified by reports of commissions, mental health research, and the voices of people with psychiatric disabilities and their advocates. Mental health organizations are pressured from all corners to develop recovery-oriented practices and systems. Some mental health leaders have distinguished themselves by their capacity to initiate this needed change. We set out to learn from these successful transformational leaders.

During the course of writing this book, we were amazed and heartened by the leaders' accounts of their leadership experiences. Many leaders were nominated by us and their peers as people who had brought about positive change in their organizations. All leaders we approached (save one) consented to be interviewed. Each leader agreed to be tape recorded and spoke with one of us for one to two hours. They were informative, modest, and self-critical. What we learned from these leaders about leadership in public mental health settings provides the foundation of this book. We hope you learn from reading it, as we learned from writing it.

WILLIAM A. ANTHONY
KEVIN ANN HUCKSHORN

ACKNOWLEDGMENTS

Writing this book has been an exciting and humbling experience. Expecting mental health leaders, working difficult and busy jobs, to give up hours of their time to be interviewed and to review transcripts was, in retrospect, quite optimistic of us. To discover that these same leaders not only would take this time, but also would have the courage to be so forthcoming, so direct, and so open to answering our questions was much appreciated. As such, we are extremely grateful to the following individuals (in order of initial appearance in this work), without whom this book would have remained only a concept.

We would like to thank Len Stein, Terry Cline, Carlos Brandenburg, Michael Hogan, James Reinhard, Cynthia Barker, Raul Almazar, Gene Johnson, Joan Erney, Margaret Beard, Rupert Goetz, Tony Zipple, Robert Quam, Kim Ingram, Pablo Hernandez, Charles Curie, Richard Surles, Tom Lane, Sandy Forquer, Kathy Muscari, Mary Alice Brown, King Davis, Kathryn Power, Larry Miller, Elizabeth Childs, Larry Kohn, Linda Rosenberg, Steven Mayberg, Paolo del Vecchio, Renata Henry, Sam Tsemberis, Dori Hutchinson, Cheryl Gagne, Martha Long, Judi Chamberlin, David Shern, Joe Swinford, Scott Graham, Sal Barbera, Judy Trysnicki, Gayle Bluebird, Dennis Rice, Estelle Douglas, Thomas Kirk, Lori Ashcraft, Bob Williams, Pam Womack, Susan Dempsey, Dennis Rice, Joseph Parks, and Patricia Kramer. Their consistent and passionate commitment to the people they serve and the staff they supervise is a courageous and illuminating testament to what transformational leadership is all about.

The authors also would like to honor the consumers and peers in our mental health systems who experience daily the outcomes resulting from the quality of the leadership in the settings where they seek or provide services. Their courage is awe inspiring, their input immeasurably valuable, and their experiences laden with learning for those who stop to listen.

Last, but certainly not least, the writing of this book also was informed by our own life and work experiences—the people who mentored us, the staff who taught us, and the people we served who provided the greatest insights into our own beliefs about transformational leadership. Not all of these people can be remembered or recognized here, but we would like to acknowledge some of them.

Bill would like to thank his family, who taught him about the power of interpersonal relationships; and to his colleagues at the Center for Psychiatric Rehabilitation, who understand the importance of relationships in bringing about change. A special recognition to Mikal Cohen, who helped conceive this project; and to Robert Carkhuff, whose insights on leadership are reflected throughout this work.

Kevin would like to thank her parents, Dr. and Mrs. Robert J. Huckshorn for consistently role modeling a most important human value, to "give back to the world," as they have done in their respective careers and lives. Second, Kevin would like to recognize three of her early and most powerful mentors, Alan Braunstein, PhD; Anne J. Boykin, PhD, MN, BSN; and Theris Touhy, DNP, APRN, BC, who taught her about the supreme importance of valuing consumer and family experiences above all other priorities.

We also acknowledge the many and marvelous talents of Linda Getgen, who edited, designed, and produced this book; and the thoroughness and patience of Sue McNamara, who painstakingly proofread the final text.

Introduction

Leadership remains an art as well as a science—some of the tools of leadership are not simply the tools of science—some are the tools of the self.
—*William A. Anthony*

There are questions many of us in the mental health field have thought about repeatedly. Such as:

- Why do some organizations prosper while others deteriorate?

- Why do some organizations flourish during a period of change while others calcify?

- Why do some organizations, previously known for their mediocrity, become exemplary organizations?

For years questions such as these have intrigued, puzzled, and bothered people in the mental health field (Anthony, 1993a). They often are summarized in the plaintive question of advocates, taxpayers, consumers, administrators, and practitioners—"Why isn't our program progressing as well as theirs?" Indeed, it is clear that there are some state departments of mental health, mental health centers, hospitals, rehabilitation centers, or individual units or programs that are just more advanced than others.

It is the thesis of this book that many, if not most, of the fundamental differences between organizations are due to differences in the quality and effectiveness of the leadership. The focus of this book is on the leadership within those organizations that serve people with severe mental illnesses. Big or small, public or private, independent of professional discipline, the book's spotlight is on the leadership as a major source of what makes one mental health organization more successful than another.

Principled Leadership is also a call for the development of a new type of leader. Leaders are urgently needed who can respond to the mental health field's new paradigms and challenges, as outlined in this introductory chapter. Especially needed are leaders who respond to these new opportunities with the requisite direction and strategies.

THE NEED FOR LEADERSHIP IN MENTAL HEALTH

As a result of many new developments in the mental health field, the need for leadership in serving persons with severe mental illnesses has never been greater. As we begin the 21st century, change seems to be the only constant factor. Leadership is needed to take advantage of the opportunities that accompany environments characterized, not only by constant change, but by a change so dramatic that the very foundation of the mental health system is being built anew. Some of these changes are due to the evolution of the field itself, such as a better understanding of the comprehensive needs, wants, and potential of persons who have serious mental illnesses. Others have been thrust on the field by forces operating in society in general, such as the movement toward managed care; the increasingly articulate and powerful voices of the people our field serves; the release of the first surgeon general's report on mental health in 1999 (U.S. Department of Health and Human Services, 1999); the Institute of Medicine's *Crossing the Quality Chasm* series (2001, 2005); and the *President's New Freedom Commission's Report on Mental Health Care in America* (2003).

> It is the thesis of this book that many, if not most, of the fundamental differences between organizations are due to differences in the quality and effectiveness of the leadership.

The most telling changes, however, will be driven by new ways of thinking that now exist with respect to the consequences of serious mental conditions, as well as the potential for recovery from these illnesses. Concerning the consequences of mental illnesses, previously the negative effects of mental illnesses were seen primarily as symptomatic impairments of mood or thought. This is no longer the case. The emergence of the rehabilitation paradigm has enlarged the potential consequences of severe mental illnesses to include not only symptom impairment but also dysfunction, disability, and disadvantage (Anthony, 1979; Anthony, Cohen, Farkas & Gagne, 2002). The importance of psychiatric rehabilitation services to address the now apparent, more comprehensive needs of people with serious mental illnesses was emphasized by the Community Support Program, initiated by the National Institute of Mental Health in the late 1970s (Turner & TenHoor, 1978). Gradually over the last quarter century, the mental health system not only became concerned with how to impact the person's impairment or symptoms, but also the person's ability to perform tasks (dysfunction), roles (disability), and deal with the discrimination and poverty (disadvantage) that he or she may face. (See table 1.)

The philosophy underlying psychiatric rehabilitation also brought to the field of mental health its unique value base that emphasizes values such as a person's involvement, choice, strengths, and growth potential, as well as outcome accountability for providers (Anthony, 1979). The inclusion of a rehabilitation paradigm and the push toward community support services (Turner & Shifren, 1979) enlarged the scope of the mental health system and its values, and challenged the leadership to think more comprehensively and respectfully about how to help people with serious mental illnesses. Outcomes related to improving people's skills; impacting people's residential, vocational, and educational statuses; increasing people's satisfaction, as well as reducing the effects of poverty and discrimination on people with mental conditions began to be included within the concerns of mental health leadership.

> The other more recent, dramatic major change within the mental health field itself has been the growing acknowledgment that people with severe mental illnesses can and do recover.

The other more recent, dramatic major change within the mental health field itself has been the growing acknowledgment that people with severe mental illnesses can and do recover (Anthony, 1993b, 2000; Deegan, 1988). While there are many definitions of recovery from severe mental illnesses (Ralph, 2000), a succinct and straightforward definition is, "the development of

Table 1—The Psychiatric Rehabilitation Model: The Negative Impact of a Severe Mental Illness

Stages ➤	I. Impairment ➤	II. Dysfunction	III. Disability	IV. Disadvantage
Definitions	Any loss or abnormality of psychological, physiological, or anatomical structure or function	Any restriction or lack of ability to perform an activity or task in the manner or within the range considered normal for a human being	Any restriction or lack of ability to perform a role in the manner or within the range considered normal for a human being	A lack of opportunity for an individual that limits or prevents the performance of an activity or the fulfillment of a role that is normal (depending on age, sex, social, cultural factors) for that individual
Examples ➤	Hallucinations, delusions, depression	Lack of work adjustment skills, social skills, ADL skills	Unemployment, homelessness	Discrimination and poverty

Adapted from: Anthony, W.A., Cohen, M.R., & Farkas, M.D. (1990). *Psychiatric rehabilitation.* Boston: Boston University, Center for Psychiatric Rehabilitation.

new meaning and purpose as one grows beyond the catastrophe of a severe mental illness" (Anthony, 1993b). Consensus has been achieved on what some of the major characteristics are included in this new vision of recovery. As described in a report of a consensus conference (del Vecchio & Fricks, 2007), these dimensions include such fundamental elements and principles as self direction, individualized and person-centered interventions, strengths based focus, responsibility and hope. The bottom line is that we now know that the majority of people with severe mental illnesses do not need to get worse. This progressive and worsening illness paradigm, upon which most of the mental health service direction of the 20th century was based, is no longer the case. Adequate supports and relevant services provided in a way that empowers people to manage their own illness can result in growth, development, healing, and recovery.

This paradigm of recovery was largely absent from the last century's diagnostic schemes (American Psychiatric Association, 1987, 2000) and maintenance-type interventions (Bachrach, 1976; Grob, 1983; President's New Freedom Commission on Mental Health, 2003). Even worse, for much of the previous century, throughout North America and Europe, not only were people with severe mental illnesses not expected to recover, they often were dehumanized and devalued by both society and treatment professionals alike (Braslow, 1997, 1995; Grob, 1994a, 1994b, 1996; Micale & Porter, 1994). The traditional and pessimistic view that people with mental illnesses lacked potential for growth and change, and responded only to interventions designed to prevent deterioration, has gradually changed (Coyle & Williams, 2001; Hinshaw & Cicchetti, 2000). As a result, within the last several decades, state mental health systems have witnessed a major shift in the conceptualization of how mental health care should be delivered. Most state mental health systems no longer view the course of serious mental illnesses as necessarily deteriorative (Sartorius, Gulbinat, Harrison, Laska & Siegel, 1996; Harrison, Hopper, Craig, Laska & Siegel, 2001; Harding Brooks, Ashikaga, et al., 1987a, 1987b; DeSisto, Harding, McCormick, 1995a). The recovery paradigm began to guide policies and practice in many individual states (see for example, Beale & Lambric, 1995; Jacobson & Curtis, 2000; Legislative

Summer Study Committee of the Vermont Division of Mental Health, 1996; State of Nebraska, 1997; State of Wisconsin Blue Ribbon Commission on Mental Health, 1997), and more recently the federal government (President's New Freedom Commission on Mental Health, 2003), as well as other countries, such as New Zealand (Lapsley, Nikora & Black, 2002).

The significant challenge for mental health leadership is the fact that mental health systems, developed over the last century and which still exist today, have been built on the mistaken assumption that serious mental illnesses are almost universally associated with a poor prognosis for recovery (American Psychiatric Association, 1987; President's New Freedom Commission on Mental Health, 2003). As a result, the current mental health practice paradigm and approach is seriously out of date, as are the academic programs that are training the newest members of our workforce (Huckshorn, 2007). Fortunately, the data are mounting that will require serious and committed leaders to transform our current care systems to one founded on a rehabilitation and recovery paradigm. It is up to the leaders in our system of care to answer the call of this new reality.

> Fortunately, the data are mounting that will require serious and committed leaders to transform our current care systems to one founded on a rehabilitation and recovery paradigm. It is up to the leaders in our system of care to answer the call of this new reality.

With respect to new data, in the last several decades, several sources of information have converged to demonstrate that people with serious mental conditions are achieving higher levels of role functioning, subjective well-being, and much improved adjustment than had previously been considered. One source of information is the writing of people with mental illnesses who have recounted numerous instances of recovery (e.g., Anonymous, 1989; Deegan 1988; Houghton, 1982; Leete, 1989; McDermott, 1990; Unzicker, 1989). Another source of knowledge is the synthesis and dissemination (Harding, 1994; 2003) of long-term outcome studies, which suggested that a significant percentage of people with serious mental illnesses were dramatically improving over time. In 2003, Harding reviewed ten U. S. and international longitudinal studies of 20 to 30 years duration demonstrating the recovery and community integration of many people with schizophrenia and other serious mental illnesses (Bleuler, 1972; Ciompi & Müller, 1976; Desisto, Harding et al., 1995a, 1995b; Harding, Brooks et al., 1987a, 1987b; Hinterhuber, 1973; Huber, Gross & Schuttler, 1979; Kreditor, 1977; Marinow, 1974; Ogawa et al., 1987; Tsuang, Woolson & Fleming, 1979). A final source of data are the research studies suggesting that substantial improvements in role functioning can be effected through mental health and rehabilitation interventions (e.g., Bond et al., 2001; Cook & Razzano, 2000; Drake et al., 1996; 1999; Mueser, et al., 2002).

In addition to challenges to leaders brought about by the new knowledge underlying the paradigms of rehabilitation and recovery, the way the entire system of mental health services has been organized is changing dramatically. Private managed care systems are being expanded to provide services to consumers of mental health services who are covered by publicly funded dollars. Many states are consolidating their state hospitals (a euphemism for state hospital closures). Capitation rather than fee-for-service is becoming an accepted payment method.

Leaders in the 21st century must lead in this unsettling time. Seemingly different concepts or procedures are being stressed simultaneously. There is an emphasis on more quality services at the same time services are being curtailed in the spirit of cost containment. Ongoing monitoring must include both subjective and objective outcome indicators. New medication interventions are now known not to be "the be-all and end-all" that was hoped for in the late 1990s (Swartz et al., 2007). While, periodically there is a renewed interest about the advantages of asylum, a much stronger focus on community integration remains. There is an increasing emphasis on involuntary procedures (such as outpatient commitment), yet at the same time the principle of consumer choice is being promoted. The private sector has entered the public service delivery system in some states—and is being warmly received by some and shunned by others.

The need for effective and principled leadership is unremitting. New paradigms, a new vision of recovery, a developing knowledge base, new organizational structures and financing schemes must become part of the leader's lexicon. New concepts, principles, and settings materialize regularly. It is in this context that effective leadership is required, to resolve conflicts and pursue a new direction. Leadership is needed to guide us through changes stimulated by new concepts, principles and settings; leadership is needed to interpret the impacts of new paradigms; leadership is needed to illuminate the common themes underlying apparent differences. The need for effective mental health leadership has never been stronger.

The challenge to transform the mental health system has been made at the highest levels of government (Curie, 2005; President's New Freedom Commission on Mental Health, 2003). By transformation these leaders don't mean change at the margins of the system, but at its very core. This kind of transformative shift in paradigms, mission, and vision will require the kind of change that Quinn talks about (Quinn, 1996). He says that "change can be incremental or deep"...and that "the former is the more familiar to most of us than the latter." Quinn defines "deep change" as more similar to revolutions as such change includes new ways of thinking and behaving that are discontinuous with the past and irreversible once begun. Quinn describes "Deep change"..."as walking naked into uncertainty" and calls this true transformational change (Quinn, 1996, p. 3). True transformation of the entire system of mental health care is the means to realizing a system built on a recovery and rehabilitation paradigm. Such a transformation demands strong and effective leadership (Anthony, 2004; Mazade, 2005).

LEADERSHIP AND PUBLICLY FUNDED ORGANIZATIONS

It is not uncommon to think of the impact of leadership on business or political organizations. Leaders in these fields have been credited with "turning a company around" or "restoring faith in the system." In contrast, very little discussion is held about leadership's role in human services, including services to people who have been diagnosed with serious mental conditions. *Principled Leadership* has been written for the audience of committed and capable leaders needed to guide the mental health public sector, as well as those leaders in private and not-for-profit mental health systems of care. We often share the provision of care to the same people and their families; the leadership principles and tasks detailed in *Principled Leadership* can apply to all mental health providers.

Mental health leadership presents unique challenges to one's leadership capacity. These unique threats and opportunities are related to the fact that people who are serving folks with psychiatric disabilities are typically funded, either partially or totally, by taxpayer dollars. Whether the funds come from the state legislatures, the state departments of mental health, from counties, and/or federal dollars (through Medicaid or Medicare and the SAMHSA Mental Health Block grants in the United States), or still other sources, services to people with severe mental illnesses often are seen as taxpayer supported. Even if the organization is a privately managed care firm or a private nonprofit agency, the presence of a significant amount of public dollars makes the leadership pressures unique. Inefficiency and ineffectiveness are seen as a drain on the taxpayers' pocketbook and a further betrayal of the public trust. Leaders in mental health have different people looking over their shoulders than do their counterparts in business settings.

Consider the environment in which the mental health leader works. Executive and legislative bodies regularly oversee and change the organization's budget. Court rulings may quickly alter how services are provided. The media is on the alert for the appearance of mismanagement. Citizen boards and individual taxpayers provide oversight. Advocacy groups add to the pressures to perform. Of course this does not mean that effective leadership is impossible in organizations funded by public dollars—but it is complicated. Furthermore, many of these overseers have little knowledge about the complexities of delivering public mental health services. Also, leaders operating in publicly funded organizations typically do not have the opportunity to reward their followers with extrinsic rewards, such as bonuses and incentive pay.

LEVELS OF LEADERSHIP

Like the privately funded sector, leadership in the publicly funded arena occurs at all levels. A hospital ward, a component of a community mental health center, a program in a clinic, a residential setting, a work unit in a vocational program, a self-help program; each of these are settings that require leadership. The information explosion has created organizations that expect more leadership at more circumscribed organizational levels. Leadership is not limited to the highest levels of an organization, such as CEO, executive director, or unit chief levels. Leadership behaviors are now required at all organizational levels. Routine, centralized, and exclusive decision making at higher or broader organizational levels now is seen as inefficient as it misses the tremendous benefits that come from the organization's human capital and the people being served.

Every staff person can act like "the CEO" in his or her own sphere of influence, no matter how broad or circumscribed, and indeed, this kind of work is what will lead to successful transformation of the mental health system.

WHAT IS LEADERSHIP?

If a relatively high position on the organizational chart does not uniquely define leadership, then what does? Over four decades ago, Vance Packard (1962) defined leadership in the following statement. "In essence leadership appears to be the art of getting others to want to do something you are convinced should be done" (p. 170). Fortunately, later definitions have modified Packard's leadership definition. Possibly the most relevant is Gary Wills (1994) definition: "the leader is one who mobilizes others towards a goal shared by leaders and followers" (p. 17). Both definitions infer the importance of "others," "goals," and "movement." Stressed in the later definition by Wills, and consistent with other current concepts of leadership, is the phrase "shared goals" as compared to a goal that the leader alone is "convinced needs to be done." Implied by its absence is the leaders' use of explicit force, even when one's followers don't want that goal or can't understand the direction.

Another way of understanding the definition of leadership is to look at the defining parameters of leadership. Wills (1994) states that there are three elements of leadership—leaders, followers, and goals. Nanus (1992) has added the environment as a critical element, that is, most leaders exercise their leadership within an organization that has some identifiable boundaries and resources within which the leader is free to operate. Combining the analyses of Wills and Nanus, the critical elements of leadership seem to be leaders, followers, goals, and an organization with identifiable boundaries and resources. We add the dimension of a shared vision. (See chapter 1 for examples of the power of a shared vision.) Thus, we define leadership as creating a shared vision and mobilizing others toward specific organizational goals consistent with the vision.

> We define leadership as creating a shared vision and mobilizing others toward specific organizational goals consistent with the vision.

MANAGERS AND LEADERS

Sometimes it is easier to understand the definition of leadership by contrasting the stereotypical descriptions of managers and leaders. Bennis and Nanus (Bennis, 1989; Bennis & Nanus, 1985; Nanus, 1992) have without a doubt articulated the distinction between management and leadership most artfully. While managers are skilled in solving problems, leaders build the organization's future. Leaders are more apt to inspire, influence, and guide while managers are more apt to control and administer. Effective leaders create new possibilities (Carkhuff & Berenson, 2000a, 2000b). In the field of mental health, leadership and management are not mutually exclusive, nor is one more needed than the other. In mental health, leaders in smaller organizations or units of organizations are often also managers. Many leaders emerge from managerial roles. However, because the functioning and goals of leaders and managers are so very different, good mental health managers are not always good mental health leaders—and vice versa.

CAN LEADERSHIP BE TAUGHT?

But from where will these new leaders emerge? Undoubtedly they will come from the ranks of mental health staff, students, and managers. While some leaders are "born leaders" many are "made." Kouzes and Posner (1995) describe three different ways in which the development of new leaders can be improved. Leaders, in essence, learn to lead by 1) trial and error, 2) from other people, and 3) from education and training.

In the field of mental health, most leaders learned about leadership through trial and error. Unfortunately their errors in leadership were other people's trials! It is certainly true that one learns to lead by having the opportunity to lead. However, leading by doing the task of leading does not ensure that one ever learns to do it well. It seems that the trial and error method of learning to lead should be combined with the other two methods in order to improve leadership effectiveness. Experience is a great teacher of leaders but some people only have one experience and repeat that same experience over and over again in new situations. Other leaders never seem to take the time, nor are they encouraged to reflect on and discuss with others their previous learning experiences. It is this time for reflection that allows for insights about one's own leadership to be developed.

Mental health leaders also can learn from other leaders; leaders from whom they have been led personally, or from leaders in the field at large. Would-be leaders themselves experience the effect of good and bad leadership. Once again, in order to learn from other leaders, it is necessary to reflect on one's discrimination about what makes one a good or poor leader. While no one wants to be led by an ineffective leader, in this type of situation one still can learn what not to do. If you can't learn about leadership from your own personal experience of effective leaders, the next best thing is to learn from acknowledged leaders in the field. Read what they have written, attend conferences at which they speak, find their followers and speak to them. If you can't interview the leaders themselves, interview their followers.

The final method of learning to be a leader is, by itself, the least important strategy. The skills of leadership are not learned simply by classroom education and training. It is difficult to learn leadership solely in a classroom. Indeed, what classrooms offer best is a chance to reflect in a group on the common experiences of leadership, and to interview and read about acknowledged leaders in the field. Interestingly, classroom settings that teach interpersonal skills or problem solving skills are teaching some of the building blocks of leadership. In the field of mental health, interpersonal skills and problem solving skills often are thought of as clinical skills rather than leadership skills. However, some of the same skills that make someone a good clinician also are fundamental to effective leadership.

This book would have no purpose if one did not assume that leadership can be improved. By reflecting on one's own experience of leading or being led, and by learning from acknowledged leaders in the field, one can indeed become a better leader. Each one of us has leadership potential. Most of us who are committed to the field of mental health will at some point in our career have the opportunity to lead, if not an entire state mental health system; a hospital, mental health center, rehabilitation center, outpatient clinic, a self-help group, or a unit or program within these larger entities. Without skilled leadership at the program or unit level, the leaders of these larger organizations will not be successful. Many of us will be leaders and followers simultaneously. For example, we might be leading an individual program in a managed care network and following the leadership of network director; or leading a program in a hospital unit and following the direction of the unit chief.

Leaders try to create the system, program, and/or unit in which mental health practitioners can do good work and in which consumers can prosper. The task of mental health leadership is to ensure that the process of helping can take place. The goal of mental health leadership is to increase the probability that people with severe mental illnesses are helped to recover in a setting and through a process that is both effective and efficient.

THE PURPOSE OF THIS TEXT

This text is designed for the current and future leaders who work or plan to work in mental health settings. The text explains and illustrates the leadership principles and accompanying tasks that acknowledged leaders in the mental health field have identified as critical for effectiveness and change sustainability. Based on interviews with leaders throughout the country, the author's eight leadership principles are advanced. By understanding these principles, by reading examples of these principles in action, and by reflecting on one's own personal development as a leader in relation to these principles, current and would-be leaders can improve their own leadership performance.

The leaders whose interviews form the foundation of this book are considered to be effective leaders by their peers. Some are well know nationally, others are known only by their local followers. All have, at one time in their career, led an organization or an organizational component that provided direct services to people with serious mental illnesses. Some possess a variety of formal mental health credentials; others possess none. Their leadership achievements have each been guided by one or more of the eight principles of leadership described in this text. They have shared their personal experiences in relation to these principles. In so doing they have allowed others to profit from their own leadership accomplishments. The analysis of these eight leadership principles and the experiences of leaders in relation to them provide the grist for readers of this book to reflect on and discuss the field of mental health leadership.

Historically, the opportunity to learn about the principles of mental health leadership and the experiences of mental health leaders has been rare indeed. As mentioned previously, leadership courses and texts are focused routinely on leaders in the corporate sector. Very little attention is paid to leadership issues in the publicly funded sector, and especially in the mental health field. According to Drucker (1996), however, the nonprofit sector has the largest number of leadership jobs in the United States and the greatest opportunities for growth. It is the public sector from which exemplary leaders of the future may emerge. As Handy (1996) has suggested:

> Until and unless business creates a cause, bigger and more embracing than enhancement of the shareholders, it will have few great leaders. We are more likely to find them in the nonprofit arena. If that is so, than that sector may yet become the training ground for business and perhaps even politics (p. 9).

As previously discussed, the leadership challenges in public mental health arenas are considerable. Mental health leaders are subject to directives from all levels of executive and legislative bodies, the judicial system's constant interpretation of mandates and boundaries, the machinations of special interest groups, unmatched media focus, and budget decisions beyond their control. This text provides the leadership principles and experiences of our current leaders as a point of departure in our journey to improve the knowledge base in the field of mental health leadership.

PRINCIPLED LEADERSHIP

What is meant by the title of this book? Principled leadership is characterized in two different ways. The most straightforward explanation is that the focus of this book is on those principles that guide effective leaders' actions. Answers are sought to the questions about the common principles and accompanying tasks that guided leaders in creating, building, and/or maintaining needed services. Examples from the leader's work are used to illustrate the principles in real life detail, and not to describe each leader's characteristics or the components of the system that they led.

Leadership also is referred to as "principled" because the services provided by the leader's organization are designed to help people recover from serious mental illnesses. We were concerned only with learning from leaders whose organization was moving toward increasing the opportunities for people to recover as compared to leaders whose primary concern was financial viability or maintaining the status quo. These leaders' strategies for changing their organizations differed; the place where they started from varied; the characteristics of their organizations, their personalities, and their strengths did not conform to one model; but universally held was their belief that promoting recovery from severe mental illnesses was the direction their organization must pursue. In that context, the leaders included in this text were "principled" in pursuing this new paradigm of recovery.

> We were concerned only with learning from leaders whose organization was moving toward increasing the opportunities for people to recover as compared to leaders whose primary concern was financial viability or maintaining the status quo.

The list of eight principles can be found in table 2. Each of the chapters following this introductory chapter examines each principle. (Principle 1 is the focus of chapter 1, principle 2 in chapter 2, and so on.) The concluding chapter makes some final points, and overviews this book's findings with popular theories and scholarly writings about leadership. The beginning of each chapter includes a table that lists the tasks relevant to the principle that is focused on in that particular chapter. The entire list of principles and accompanying tasks can be found in appendix A.

THE PROCESS OF WRITING THIS TEXT

The process leading to the publication of this book has been a long one. In the late 1990s one of us (WA) designed a course in "mental health leadership." He invited leaders from around the country to lecture, in that course, on the basic principles that guided their work. The 16 leaders chosen to lecture were known to him as leaders who had been trying to change the segregated,

Table 2—The Eight Principles of Leadership

Principle 1. Leaders communicate a shared vision.

Principle 2. Leaders centralize by mission and decentralize by operations.

Principle 3. Leaders create an organizational culture that identifies and tries to live by key values.

Principle 4. Leaders create an organizational structure and culture that empowers their employees and themselves.

Principle 5. Leaders ensure that staff are trained in a human technology that can translate vision into reality.

Principle 6. Leaders relate constructively to employees.

Principle 7. Leaders access and use information to make change a constant ingredient of their organization.

Principle 8. Leaders build their organization around exemplary performers.

authoritarian, and/or restrictive way that services of the last century often were organized. The course was structured around 12 principles that leaders in business seemed to favor; the course was taught for two consecutive years. Based on the mental health leaders' comments, examples, and suggestions, the principles were refined and reduced to eight, and tasks attached to each principle. It was at that point that KH joined the effort.

Another round of leadership interviews were conducted. Thirty-six leaders were asked to consent to be interviewed. (Two leaders from the initial group were re-interviewed.) We selected the leaders to be interviewed based on their ability to create significant change in their organization toward a consumer centered, non-coercive, and accountable system of care that facilitates recovery for people with severe mental illnesses. Over our decades long careers in the field of mental health, the authors of this book have visited every state in the union, most states significantly more times than once. We nominated leaders to be interviewed that we agreed were recovery oriented. We asked other leaders for nominations. For reasons of redundancy and length, many more leaders were nominated than could be included in this book. And we thank all who spoke to us about their leadership competencies, their challenges, their confusions, and their personal experiences.

We do not claim that the leaders interviewed for this book were "perfect leaders," as we know of no such breed. What we confirm is the fact that they were recovery oriented and that they were able to provide examples of times their leadership was guided by one or more of the principles advanced in this book. Ultimately, the validity of our leadership selection process for *Principled Leadership* will be reflected in the usefulness of this book to current and future leaders. As the authors, we believe the leaders' accounts of their leadership activities will attest to the reason for their inclusion in this text on *Principled Leadership.*

Just as not all the nominated leaders could be included in *Principled Leadership,* neither could most of the material obtained from the selected leaders. Each interview was tape recorded and typically lasted over an hour. The complete interview was transcribed and then edited by KH, reviewed by WA, and excerpts of the interview were entered into the book. Excerpts were drawn from the interviews to illustrate leadership principles and tasks. KH conducted the bulk of the second round of interviews. The letter and form requesting an interview that was sent to prospective interviewees may be found in appendix B. All but one of the leaders contacted agreed to be included in the text. In the interests of time, several individuals emailed their responses rather than be interviewed.

The quotes from the leaders used in this book are verbatim, with one significant exception to the verbatim rule. When people are interviewed, they sometimes do not talk in complete sentences or perfect syntax. When we ourselves have been interviewed for material that eventually will be converted to written text, we routinely request that the authors revise our spoken word when necessary to make it comprehensible when written. We don't want the substance changed but the syntax is a different matter! We did the same when we converted the spoken word to written text for this book. To be true to the interview format, we did not try to rewrite the interviews as if they were written prose. Thus the reader often can recognize that the phrasing in the leader's quoted ideas reflects the words as spoken, not as he or she would have written them. However, when absolutely necessary we have modified the wording to make the ideas flow logically and be more understandable when converted to written form. We have not identified in the written text where this re-phrasing has been done. We did check with the interviewees when transcription was difficult or there were significant questions about content.

> We do not claim that the leaders interviewed for this book were "perfect leaders," as we know of no such breed. What we confirm is the fact that they were recovery oriented and that they were able to provide examples of times their leadership was guided by one or more of the principles advanced in this book.

We conducted all the interviews without advancing any preconceived theory about leadership. We wanted the leaders to talk about their own experiences, and not how they fit or did not fit a theory of leadership.

While the original set of 12 principles drew from the business and leadership literature available up until the mid-90s, once we had drafted the 8 principles and their related tasks based on the first round of interviews, our next round of interviews was not guided by any new leadership literature. The first draft of the eight principles and tasks continued to be modified by the later round of interviews. In the concluding chapter, we compare and contrast the eight leadership principles and accompanying tasks with some of the prevailing literature on leadership.

In summary, in the field of mental health leadership, the challenge to transform what we do, the opportunity to make such a transformation happen, and the knowledge base to support that transformation are all converging. Individuals who are or will be making their careers in mental health need to understand the principles that other leaders have used to transform their organizations to move toward meeting the new challenges of the 21st century.

1

Leaders communicate a shared vision.

- The leader makes sure the vision is a shared vision.

- The leader constantly communicates the vision.

- The leader clearly communicates the vision.

- The leader uses the vision to inspire the staff.

- The leader identifies the relevance of the vision to the organization's consumers.

- The leader lives a life compatible with the vision.

- The leader is able to persuade others of the potency of the vision.

- The leader uses the vision to shape the future.

Leaders communicate a shared vision.

A shared organizational vision is like an organizational magnet—it attracts to it only people with special characteristics

—*William A. Anthony*

In the Old Testament there is a famous line that reads, "Where there is no vision the people perish." Thousands of years after the Old Testament was written, President George Herbert Walker Bush admitted to having trouble understanding what he called "the vision thing." The importance of having a vision—personal, organizational, or both—has been alluded to since the beginning of time itself. Yet, it may be talked about more than it is understood and practiced. This seems to be particularly true in the field of mental health.

The field of mental health, similar to former President George H. W. Bush, has not been comfortable with this "vision thing." In absence of a vision, the field of mental health has rallied itself around popular movements. These include, for example, institutionalization, deinstitutionalization, "case management," and financing based on managed care or other capitated funding models. However, these movements are not visionary because they do not indicate how the consumer of mental health services will benefit, be impacted, nor what person-centered outcomes are anticipated. Instead, these movements talk about how the service system will change—but not the *hoped for* changes for the consumers of services. In other areas, such as business and industry, a vision is used to provide an overriding purpose or goal, promote change, and progress to a more advanced organization or initiative that results in satisfied customers. For example, in the 1960s NASA had a vision, albeit in retrospect a sexist one. Their vision was to "put a man on the moon in this decade." It was a clear, straightforward vision, and it successfully marshaled the talent and dollars of the entire country. Now NASA does not have a comparable new vision—and subsequently fewer resources. It is difficult for the citizenry to rally around ideas lacking visionary power, such as—build a space lab, build bigger rockets, fix a telescope, or build another space shuttle.

The cancer field has a vision. It is to "cure cancer in our lifetime," which is a straightforward, understandable, succinct vision. This vision speaks clearly to what people living with cancer can expect if the vision is achieved. And the continued resources that support this vision are laudable. A vision is a credible, picture or image of the future. A vision is something that we are not now achieving but believe is possible. It pulls us toward the future. A vision is hopeful and attractive. It somehow makes our goals come closer. While currently many cancers cannot be cured, the vision of curing cancer in our lifetime harnesses the resources, talents, and commitment that are needed to pursue this vision.

> The simpler the vision can be portrayed, the greater its chances of directing the organization and perhaps influencing the entire field in which it has relevance.

The leaders in some mental health organizations have used statements of vision for similar purposes. The leader's organization is energized and mobilized by a shared vision of what is possible for the consumers they serve. Leaders understand that their staffs are motivated by their belief in the organization's purpose. Mental health work is more than just achieving profits, living within one's budget, and/or organizational and job survival or satisfaction. It is about supporting the hopes and dreams of the consumers it serves that parlay into very energized and meaningful work for the people who serve them.

What is surprising about a vision is how simple, in presentation, vision statements really are. "Cure cancer in our lifetime," "put a man on the moon in this decade" are not complex visioning statements. The simpler the vision can be portrayed, the greater its chances of directing the organization and perhaps influencing the entire field in which it has relevance. It is often the leaders' ability to simplify and succinctly communicate the vision that makes the vision take hold.

In the early 1970s a young psychiatrist, named Len Stein, and his associates, Mary Ann Test and Arnold Marx, developed a vision of what people with psychiatric disabilities could expect from the treatment system. This vision has had a lasting impact on the field of mental health. As recounted to us by Len Stein, it was a simple yet powerful vision. In essence, Stein believed that people with severe mental illnesses could achieve a stable life in the community *by being treated in the community* rather than in state hospitals. Len believed that treating people with severe mental conditions, in the community, would not only avoid the negative side effects of institutionalization but also create new opportunities for learning and personal growth that could only be experienced in the more normalized and comfortable local "community" where the person had chosen to live. Accordingly, he and his colleagues designed a treatment intervention that essentially transferred existing hospital staff into the community and diverted people, who would otherwise have been hospitalized, into their natural community for their treatment (Stein & Test, 1978, 1980). At the time, this vision was almost a heretical notion. The intervention, based on this vision, came to be known as Assertive Community Treatment (ACT), and almost three decades after its inception, it remains the most widely studied community-based and evidenced-based intervention. (Thompson et al., 1990).

Len stated that while he was initiating the program he "always kept his focus on the bull's-eye" of what he was trying to accomplish. Throughout the implementation of this intervention, there were many harsh and vocal critics of this program who believed that the proper and only place for treating people with severe mental illnesses was a state hospital. Len's detractors were looking

> It is often the leaders' ability to simplify and succinctly communicate the vision that makes the vision take hold.

for reasons to shut down the program, and Len believes that if there had been one untimely death in the community, he and the program would have been gone. Len was passionate about the vision of community treatment, and he risked his reputation on its success. Len drove a stake in the ground around his basic vision, and his vision guided him and his staff through the many challenges to the implementation of what is now known as the ACT program. Now, thirty years later, Len's vision is an accepted fact—most all people with severe psychiatric disabilities are treated in the community. Dr. Len Stein is often referred to as the "father of community psychiatry." Unlike Len, many leaders may not have the opportunity to see their vision become reality.

A shared vision between leader and followers, as in the case of Len Stein and his colleagues, can enthuse staff and engender pride. A shared vision encourages perspective on what is trying to be accomplished. A vision lets both staff and consumers know what their role is in the intended purpose of the organization. The purpose of a healthcare organization is not just to provide services—but to somehow benefit the customer or consumer. A vision lets both the staff and consumers know what path the organization is following and toward what ultimate outcome. While the vision takes the organization down a path, it is a path with few sign posts. The vision of an organization should act as its magnetic north. Like a magnet, it pulls people in the same direction, and with effective visions, staff and others are drawn to it.

> A shared vision connects the personal beliefs of leaders and their followers and colleagues.

A shared vision connects the personal beliefs of leaders and their followers and colleagues. For example, years after Len Stein was first interviewed, Len was asked of the origin of his vision (Ashcraft & Anthony, 2005). Len credits not his psychiatry textbooks but his mother for his different way of thinking about the way people with severe mental illnesses should be treated. "My mother was the most democratic person I have ever known," Len said. He incorporated into his leadership, lessons he had learned from her, "...that no one is above you or below you." Len was strongly impacted by this lesson and brought it into his work when he did not see this concept implemented in mental hospitals at the time (Ashcraft & Anthony, 2005, p. 9).

People who are attracted to an organization and its vision, "share" the vision because it connects in a personal sense. Leaders and followers are not asked to give up their personal visions but to add the compatible organizational vision to their own. A shared vision speaks directly to what is personally important to the people in the organization and, in the best situation, the organizational vision is congruent with the personal ones in a way that allows the former to comfortably subsume the latter.

In the case of Terry Cline, and many other leaders, the process of developing a shared vision is extensive. Just after Terry Cline was interviewed he had been appointed to be the incoming administrator of the Substance Abuse and Mental Health Services Administration (SAMHSA). During his interview he talked about his leadership experience as the assistant secretary for health in Oklahoma. Prior to that position he held a joint appointment as the Oklahoma commissioner of the Department of Mental Health and Substance Abuse Services and the secretary of health. During the interview Terry spoke in detail about the development of his shared vision and mission for the Oklahoma Health Department, which included the provision of recovery-oriented services to people with serious mental illnesses.

> People who are attracted to an organization and its vision "share" the vision because it connects in a personal sense.

> We have tried, in Oklahoma, to have our vision and mission be the front and center of everything we do. We started with a strategic planning process that was based on stakeholder groups across the state. There were about 1,000 people who were involved in that stakeholder process, and we pulled together all their ideas about mental health, substance abuse, the needs, the gaps, how well we were doing, and where we needed to improve. All of that information was synthesized into a strategic plan.

Terry used the words vision and mission often. Terry went on to describe how the mission was not only shared, but also clear and persuasive to all Oklahomans.

> Our mission statement focused on promoting Healthy Communities and goes back to the Surgeon General's Report on Mental Health and the President's New Freedom Commission on Mental Health. Our mission statement emphasized that mental health and substance abuse issues are central to overall health. So our

mission statement did not even mention mental health or substance abuse. It promoted Healthy Communities, to provide the highest quality care, and enhance the well being of all Oklahomans. Our goal was to make it clear to the broader community that these issues were and are relevant to them. So we worked to make it clear that our issues have an impact on everyone; not just people who are directly impacted by mental illnesses or substance abuse issues—not just their own families or themselves. But that every Oklahoman is impacted by this system and how well we do in responding to these illnesses and preventing these illnesses, if possible. This report was a very powerful tool because it gave us the power to go out and say this is something you need to listen to. You need to listen to this message because it impacts you.

Terry recognized the importance of connecting the organizational vision to others' visions, in this case the entire citizenry of the state of Oklahoma.

Carlos Brandenburg was another leader who understood the power of a shared vision. When Carlos was interviewed, he was the administrator of Nevada's Division of Mental Health, Developmental Services and Substance Abuse. When Carlos became the division administrator for just mental health and developmental services in 1995, he recounted that:

The division did not have any vision or any mission. It was almost like a ship without a rudder. The vision is extremely important because it's something that is shared, not only by the commissioner or the leader of the organization, but it's something that all staff and consumers and key stakeholders have to buy into. The way we actually developed the vision was that we got as many people as we could from the various constituents and we got key stakeholders; for example, we got law enforcement, we got the judiciary, we got family members, we got consumers, and we got the chair of the advisory council. In our state, we have a commission that oversees mental health, so we got the chair of the commission. We got them to help us with the vision statement. And once we were able to come up with a vision statement that we all agreed on, we basically then developed the mission. Let me just share with you our vision statement. It was "to assist individuals with mental illness or developmental disabilities to realize their optimal potential as individuals and as valued citizens of their community and state."

Few leaders understand the value of collaboration on the vision better than Mike Hogan. Mike Hogan was interviewed when he was director of the Ohio Department of Mental Health, and then again just prior to his assuming leadership of the New York State Office of Mental Health. While he was Ohio director, Mike also served as chair of the President's New Freedom Commission on Mental Health (2003). (Some of his President's Commission leadership experiences can be found in chapter 2.)

Mike began working in his Ohio position three years after Ohio passed a Mental Health Act which formulated new policies, a new mission, specified a set of services, and transferred resources from hospitals to local community service boards. Prior to Mike's arrival the Ohio Department of Mental Health had begun to significantly change, with the guidance of Governor Richard Celeste and his wife, who had strong, personal interests in the delivery of mental health services, and had hired Pam Hyde to change the system. Ohio became nationally recognized as a system that had brought about significant positive system change. Mike remarked that, because of his predecessors, he did not need to create a new direction, but rather keep the momentum alive and work on the details of its implementation.

Mike strongly emphasized the collaborative nature of visioning, in which he and his leadership team cooperated in discovering and developing. According to Mike, a leader needs:

> to collaboratively discover what vision is possible in the context in which one is operating and to construct that vision in a way that adds meaning to the people participating in it. Visioning is not this lonely and brilliant task of coming up with the Gettysburg Address, but it involves a conversational approach to discovering and co-creating a shared vision....The great leader helps people identify the vision they had but didn't know they had.

Mike draws a parallel to the clinical process, where people are helped to develop their goals rather than being told of their goals.

A year after his tenure began, Mike had a retreat with his team to, among other things, develop a shared vision. The vision that was developed included such things as living in a community that is supportive and participating in activities of one's choice with the hope of good health. Mike pointed out that the words were less significant than the fact that they worked on them together. The process of developing the vision can be as important as the specific words used to describe the vision. Certain words that Mike wanted to include were not reflected in the final statement because, true to the collaborative nature of the visioning process, he believed it was not solely his vision but the team's vision.

Consistent with Mike's emphasis on the visioning process, as contrasted with the specific vision words chosen, the actual phrases included in the vision statements of the leaders interviewed for this book vary considerably, as do their words for their organization's values as detailed in chapter 3. However, what makes all the visions similar and "principled," and thus included in this book, are their universal emphases on people's growth, healthy development, recovery, and healing, etc. Notions of segregation, control, custodial care, etc., are not found in principled leaders' visions. Thus, what matters are not the differences in how principled leaders wordsmith the vision, but the similarities in how principled leaders envision the possibilities for recovery.

> The process of developing the vision can be as important as the specific words used to describe the vision.

Jim Reinhard was commissioner of Mental Health, Mental Retardation and Substance Abuse Services in Virginia when he was interviewed. He remarked on the trust that must be generated even before an organization can arrive at a shared vision.

> One of the first things that I found that I needed to do in this position, coming into this system, was to start from scratch in the area of establishing a collaborative spirit and trust among the major stakeholders. I personally felt the need to do this as I had been in a variety of roles, and it was apparent that engendering trust and collaboration was going to be the first goal even before we started talking about what the vision was to be. There had

been a lot of mistrust generated through previous administrations where the mental health system was left feeling like the state mental health authority was more interested in taking the system apart.

Jim continued on along this line of thinking.

> I really felt early on that my office had to be very clear that we were going to be highly invested in developing our mental health services. I spent some time, in the major presentations that I would make with the stakeholders at their annual meetings, for example, emphasizing the need for collaboration; that we weren't going to get anywhere unless we were speaking with the same voice. The general assembly had been getting so many different messages that they basically had thrown up their hands and said "we're not going to do anything since you can't seem to get your act together." So we really needed to get to the point that people had some trust in the process so they could rally around and realize that we were trustworthy enough to stick with the vision.

Jim's leadership team had to be aligned on the vision message, or progress would be stifled. A shared vision can begin to align the activities of the entire organization. The vision can begin to connect people to one another through this shared picture of the future to which they aspire together.

A vision can be communicated by a leader through the use of stories, metaphors, anecdotes, and quotations. Gardner (1995) believes that the leader must tell a story to their followers—a story that unfolds over time in the communications of the leader and indeed in the way the leader lives his or her life. It is within this story that the vision takes hold. Cynthia Barker of Knoxville, Tennessee had many stories of how the vision she shared took hold. When Cynthia was interviewed she was recovering from the symptoms of a mental illness while she continued to work and advocate for services for others with severe mental illnesses. At that time she was directing Project Phoenix, a "mobile" drop-in center, which took people by van to whatever events and locations in the community they wished to go. The program served about 100 people a month. The project had a van and others would use their own transportation resources to attend these community activities.

There was no drop-in center per se; people would "drop-in" to whatever sites in the community they wished. In the early 1990s, it was probably the first, and perhaps maybe the only "mobile" drop-in center in the country.

Cynthia's vision for the program that she created was to use community activities and settings in as normal a way as possible. For example, she repeatedly reminded folks that the program's van must look like a passenger van and not an agency van. She refused to use the mental health center's 15-person, white passenger vans; instead the grant she wrote was to fund a 7-person, passenger van, which was burgundy. She reminded people that a mini van was how most people ventured out in the community—not in a white, 15-person passenger van with lettering on the side. Cynthia was vigilant in ensuring the potency of the vision and not letting the program slip into other types of segregated activities or locations. She led a life compatible with the vision. Cynthia gave up her disability check when she returned to work.

> The journey down the vision path needs to make sense to the followers in terms of where they have been and where they are going.

The journey down the vision path needs to make sense to the followers in terms of where they have been and where they are going. The leader's story must fill in the background and detail so that the followers can stay on the path. The leader's staff stay on the path through the vision's appeal to both their reason and emotion. As Len Stein stated to us with respect to promoting the vision of community treatment through both reason and emotion, "...passion is important in leadership...but passion can't interfere with your good judgment." There is always a passion to a vision. Indeed for many people, it is their leaders' passionate communication of the vision which exerts the strongest force.

Part of the recovery vision for Raul Almazar, CEO of Elgin State Hospital when he was interviewed, was that he passionately wanted his organization's vision to be relevant to the organization's consumers, and thus included consumers in important organizational activities.

> One of the things that we started doing, early on, was that we changed the way we provided inservice training by combining consumers and staff trainers together. I really feel that people

need to be very clear that we have a lot of very smart consumers. Leadership dialogued a lot with staff about this. One of the things that we have done in the last two years was to change the way we developed our policies. All of our hospital policies go through our consumer council. This has allowed us to take advantage of the insights of the people we serve and reminds us of the principle, "nothing about us without us." The other thing we've done to is to have our forms also be approved by the consumer council.

One example of consumer involvement in policy development is our hospital personal safety plan. We gathered examples of different policies from across the country, and it was the consumers who developed the final product. At the very first meeting the consumer council looked at these examples and said. "Okay, why does the first question always start with—when you are agitated...? Why do you assume we are agitated to begin with?" That was so awesome. They completely turned around the safety plan.

Another thing we have done, specifically with inservices, is that we have weekly grand rounds. Consumers were first invited to grand rounds and they started to participate. Now we have consumer-hosted grand rounds. They pick the topic, we find a speaker for them, and they invite staff. For example, they have invited NAMI to talk about how to advocate for themselves, as well as community and political advocacy. They've brought people who are recovering, and who came out of the forensic system, to talk about how to deal with the stigma when you have a forensic history. Our staff benefit a lot from it, especially from the questions that our consumers ask which helps staff understand what interests consumers. I thought it was significant when, during the last Joint Commission survey, the surveyors saw that consumers were part of executive management. They were pretty blown away and said it was their first experience seeing consumers as a part of the executive team. They asked their leadership questions and one was "how effective is the communication across the different layers of organization?" The consumers said, "what do you think, we are the proof…"

Gene Johnson was interviewed while he was the president/CEO of META Services in Phoenix, Arizona. (META later change their name to Recovery Innovations.) Gene spoke passionately of how he used a clear vision to help shape the future of his organization.

> Today, at META Services our vision is, "a transformed service system that puts the person first." I say today, because while I always believed in the value of the person and thought META created services that were person-centered and honored self-determination, it was not until I began to really listen to those we served and to our staff that I realized we did not honor the person. The most dramatic example of this was in our crisis services. In Maricopa County, by 2000, META had become the crisis system. We operated the reception and evaluation centers where the police brought in people, often in shackles, for involuntary evaluations. We used locked rooms, seclusion, restraint, and forced medication. I had viewed these practices (we called them "safety interventions") as necessary and hoped they were used only as a last resort. I thought that since we only occasionally did a take down and used restraints that we were doing okay. When I began to listen to the heartbreaking stories of how the people we served had experienced these practices, I was distressed. When I began to listen to the experiences of our staff who had to carry out these practices, I found I had been misguided. We did not honor the person. We did not put the person first. I realized that as CEO I had devoted my energy to building our business, creating sound business practices (like risk management), but I had forgotten our purpose.

Gene used this very uncomfortable information and the emotion it generated to make some dramatic changes and to build a vision that would shape his organization's future.

> Out of my quiet anguish, I made a u-turn. I made a loud public declaration that we were going to stop the violence in our crisis centers; eliminate seclusion and restraint. This declaration was the organizational turning point. From this moment on, I took the message of zero restraint and seclusion everywhere. Initially staff

did not share my enthusiasm but most agreed that a different response sounded like a wonderful idea. Some were afraid and thought their CEO had "gone over the edge." But when the service users in our system heard my vision they cheered, and I became more passionate and determined. I got busy and our teams got busy; information, new policies, new training, data and tracking, and celebrations of our success. It didn't happen overnight. At one center where we had about 350 emergency visits a month, we achieved restraint elimination within eight months. The second center with a much higher volume, as many as 900 visits a month, it took two years. But it happened. Today, four years later, the violence inherent in the use of seclusions and restraint is not even a consideration. We now talk about this experience as our metaphor for transformation. The impossible is possible. We can put the person first.

Leaders use the vision to change the future. For this to occur they need to believe, like Gene Johnson, that the future actually can be changed by their present actions. When Joan Erney was interviewed, she was the commissioner of the Office of Mental Health and Substance Abuse Services in Pennsylvania. One of the most difficult tasks she had to accomplish was the closure of one of their state hospitals. Importantly, Joan made sure that hospital closure was not the vision for the state. Rather, the vision was to have people living and recovering in their own communities. Aiden Altenor was the bureau director in charge of the hospital closure task. When the expected resistances to hospital closure occurred, the argument for closure was made in terms of facilitating the vision of recovery in the community. As told to us by Joan, it was Aiden's personal passion that kept the state's focus on the recovery vision, and as a result, helped shape the future of community living in Pennsylvania.

> Leaders use the vision to change the future. For this to occur they need to believe...that the future actually can be changed by their present actions.

The stories and metaphors that accompany the vision flesh out the vision's definition. John Beard and the many leaders of Fountain House have been masterful in giving life to their vision through stories. John Beard developed Fountain House, the world's first "clubhouse," designed to help people live "vocationally active and socially satisfying lives" (Beard, Propst & Malamud, 1982, p. 47). The Fountain House model, developed by John Beard, has been replicated in hundreds of settings and dozens of countries. The basic vision of Fountain House was that people with severe mental illnesses could achieve rehabilitation through relationships built around normal activities.

While we knew John Beard personally, he died long before this leadership book was conceived. But in earlier conversations with John, we listened to his stories, and for this book we interviewed his daughter, Margaret Beard, who directed a clubhouse herself (Beard, 1983, 1992). We knew John to be a principled leader. The underlying themes of these vision-reinforcing stories told by the Fountain House leadership were always the same: they were about the people served and how the vision of a successful life in normal community activities was achieved. The first people to tell these types of stories about the success of their members were the leadership.

> Stories of how the vision had come true in people's actual lives made the vision inspirational and clear.

Later on it became the clubhouse members themselves telling their own stories in their own words. These stories of how the vision had come true in people's actual lives made the vision inspirational and clear.

Raul Almazar, at Elgin State Hospital, also believed in the potency of story to communicate a vision, and made storytelling an organizational practice.

> Another practice we adopted, that has really helped us become a successful community, has been to really encourage storytelling about our success stories. I get these through emails, and people stop me and tell me. These stories describe "someone who has been witnessed doing something right" by someone else. It's always about someone seen doing something right. The stories have been pouring in. We never tell who reported the story. What happens sometimes is that the person does not know who wrote the story and so does not know who to thank. So they feel good and maybe give back with a story of their own.

The vision of the leader also must compete in the marketplace of ideas, i.e., the larger system of which it is a part. Any change in one part of the system affects other parts of the system. Any new and powerful vision and its accompanying stories can be perceived as a threat to others' way of life. When a vision is inclusionary (for example, people with mental illnesses can be helped without being hospitalized), it denies privileged status to people who work in hospitals. Indeed, as in Len Stein's case, because the system had heretofore been conceptualized around the preeminence of hospital care, the new vision had to compete against society's prevailing opinions that were very much counter to what Len and his colleagues were trying to do.

When Rupert Goetz was interviewed, he was medical director at the Hawaii State Hospital. Prior to that he was medical director of a county mental health service in Oregon. Rupert described how in Oregon he helped develop a shared vision by seizing opportunities to persuade folks of the worthiness of the vision. While he was medical director in Oregon, his county incorporated into their vision the notion that mental health services and health services should be coordinated and integrated to the fullest degree possible. When he had the opportunity to provide psychiatric consultation to the health staff about a difficult situation in the health center, he used this as the first step in pursuing the vision toward a more coordinated and integrated mental health and health service.

It started as a consultation meeting that people got kind of jazzed about. Then I went back to my director and met with the administrators and said well, how can we formalize this process? If we could do this, we could have better care and use our services more wisely. It worked because it was a relatively small county, and both systems' leadership was strong. The word got out that consultation was available across systems. We started using a family nurse practitioner at the mental health center who was from the primary health side, and we began to provide consultation to a public health clinic on mental health education. About a year or so later, the county health department and the county mental health department literally merged under one administration. And then the county board of commissioners became involved and continued that theme. I think a leader communicating a shared vision uses a construct that is almost opportunistic. I mean the shared vision needs to be congruent with the context, and if there's some gasoline around, it may be worth waving around a match and seeing if something catches fire.

Besides being opportunistic, leaders must state the vision of their organization repeatedly. Leaders often spend incredible amounts of time communicating their vision and struggling against antagonism and/or resistance toward their vision. It just didn't make sense to some professionals as to why Cynthia Barker wouldn't use the agency van for transport. Cynthia was constantly communicating her vision of "integrated activities in the community" and why an agency van was not consistent with that vision.

When Thomas Kirk was interviewed, he was the commissioner of the Department of Mental Health and Addiction Services for Connecticut. Prior to that time, he had served as deputy commissioner when the state developed their recovery vision for the state. Kirk believed that the relative significance of the eight principles of mental health leadership, as described in this book vary depending on the particular emphasis of the state organization at any moment in time. Communicating the shared vision repeatedly to all level of staff was important to him in his beginning work as commissioner, and he did this not just through words.

> Besides being opportunistic, leaders must state the vision of their organization repeatedly.

One of the challenges in an organization such as this, where you have non-direct care people, is they don't necessarily see the relevance of what they do to the vision because they never see patients; they never see the people in the system. One of the things we tried to emphasize was how what they do relates quite directly to the people that we see in our service system. We try to have people come into the office of the commissioner; we invite them to go to one of our facilities, for a day, to see some of the programs. I remember there was one lady who said she wanted to go to one of our state-operated women's residential programs. Based on her visit, she had a better understanding of who the people are and who gets the services. So when I talk day in and day out about how we are helping people to recover their lives, she could see people whose lives we helped to recover and who were involved in the process. So the shared vision, principle one, is a very, very important one.

Tony Zipple was interviewed when he was the CEO of Thresholds in Chicago, one of the largest and well known psychosocial rehabilitation centers in the country. Tony said he never missed an opportunity to talk about the recovery vision and the evidence-based practices (EBPs) helpful in achieving it.

> I hold "town hall" meetings at eight or more places within Thresholds, once or twice a year. This is a chance to talk about changes at Thresholds and to hear and talk about staff concerns. But I also get to talk a lot about recovery and what that means at Thresholds. And I repeat it in staff trainings that I personally do. And I say it in staff meetings. And I echo it in our members' council (for direct consumers); and with the board; and other stakeholders. I get to be a cheerleader for Thresholds and its mission and you can never cheer too loudly or too often.

> I also use a lot of stories when I talk about recovery and EBPs [evidence-based practices]. Some are personal, some are about consumers, some, I have heard from others...some are not even directly from the mental health world, but they illustrate a point and make it real for people. Humor and heart are important in this. Yogi Berra and the Dalai Lama may turn up side by side in a discussion of recovery along with my collection of stories about consumers, staff, and my own successes and breathtaking failures! As a leader, you need to talk a lot about what matters in a way that sticks.

Mental health staff have seen too many fads come and go. Their experience of many new initiatives is for them to disappear when the leader gets on to something else, or when the leadership changes. Some staff so tire of this kind of pattern that they decide to just wait out new leaders, knowing someone else will come in with a new "fad." While visions are different from fads, fads are what most mental health staff know. Thus, it is critical for leaders to communicate their core vision constantly. They may communicate it differently, that is, with different metaphors, different symbols, in writing as well as verbally. But communicate it they must. If it is omitted, just once, this omission will begin to create doubt in their followers. And, as such, leaders need to attempt to sustain their vision the best that they can; in policy statements, standards, and regulations.

In Virginia, Commissioner Jim Reinhard anticipated that the vision for Virginia would:

> ...center around a recovery-oriented system and concepts like empowerment and self-determination and consumer-driven planning, resiliency, and the like. As the commissioner, and as a psychiatrist too, I began educating myself about recovery. I certainly was not an expert when I came into this job but I tried to become as much of one as I could about what recovery really meant. Also, I found that it is really necessary to commit yourself, if you want to be an expert about anything, so I committed myself to providing grand rounds in our medical schools, to talking about recovery in just about every talk I gave, keynote speeches or whatever. I related all the talks to recovery—making the point that if we were serious about transforming our system that was the only way it was going to happen. I really wanted our agency to be clearly identified as the one that was really out in front on the vision of recovery. I think most stakeholders would agree and say that they believe that the commissioner of the mental health system believed in recovery and was advocating for that; some of the major consumer voices in the Commonwealth believe that we actually get it.

Bob Quam, in his work as chief operating officer at South Florida State Hospital (run by GEO Care, Inc.), was adamant about working to sustain the new vision of the hospital by the use of written policies and procedures. This civil hospital, serving over 300 consumers with serious mental illnesses had to shift from being a long-term custodial care facility to one that used an active treatment model with much reduced lengths of stay. Bob pulled together his leadership team and worked to create long-lasting change, regardless of whomever was in the leadership positions over time. Toward this end, Bob's team created policies that included consumers hired as full-time staff with job descriptions and in state authorized positions; a consumer-run drop in center; over 80 paid positions for consumers receiving current services in employed roles; an active treatment mall; re-designed staff job descriptions; and possibly most important, implemented a new vision for a recovery-oriented system of care that used consumer's chosen language and incorporated recovery into operations in all documentation.

> Leaders must embody their vision. While a leader does not have to be perfect, or even close to it, their personal and professional life must not contradict their vision.

Leaders must embody their vision. While a leader does not have to be perfect, or even close to it, their personal and professional life must not contradict their vision. Followers are looking to elevate their leaders' stature, but they are paradoxically looking for the inconsistencies of the leader. If the leader is viewed as hypocritical in the disparity between one's communicated vision and lived actions, then the power of their leadership is mitigated. In other words, the personal and organizational visions are compatible for principled leaders. They see their life as part of the organization's vision in that their own life is part of and consistent with this larger purpose. The words of their personal visions line up with their organizational visions. Yet it is the leaders' actions and behaviors, not words alone, that demonstrate this alignment between personal and organizational vision to be true.

Kim Ingram, who was interviewed when she was the CEO of Thomasville Mental Health and Rehabilitation Center in Thomasville, Alabama, was a leader whose vision and actions were aligned. At one time the Thomasville Center was an old air base; in 1974, it was converted into a state hospital for people with mental illnesses. During the 1990s, Kim became involved in a massive organizational change process at the Thomasville Center to trans-form the Center from a custodial setting to an active rehabilitation setting. Kim had served as the acting CEO, and then later she became the permanent CEO. In 1991, Thomasville was accredited for three years by the Joint Commission on the Accreditation for Healthcare Organizations—the first time in its history the facility had received accreditation. In 1994 Thomasville was accredited once again, this time with commendation. As reported in a Birmingham, Alabama newspaper, "Thomasville scored 98 out 100 possible points during a 3-day review by the Joint Commission for the Accreditation of Healthcare Organizations...the staff and clients seem friendly and familiar. Ms. Ingram seems to know each patient by name, and they call her by name." Under the leadership of Kim and her staff the Thomasville Center, in spite of its out-of-the-way location, became a place in which national and international mental health leaders visited to learn about "the Thomasville story."

> It is the leaders' actions and behaviors, not words alone, that demonstrate this alignment between personal and organizational vision to be true.

According to Kim, Thomasville's vision is that people can choose the community environments in which they want to go to live, learn, work, or socialize. Kim believes leaders must "live their vision." She calls herself a "convert" to the importance of organizational vision. Initially, when she and a group spent time articulating the values and vision of the organization, she did not think it would be particularly useful. "I have been proven wrong on a daily basis," Kim states in retrospect. Now she thinks defining the vision is a most critical place to begin.

> The vision guides everything that we have done...allows us to make decisions...everything we do from buying equipment, to hiring staff, to programming is made relevant to the vision and mission. When we are making decisions, we ask constantly, is this a key thing that moves us toward accomplishing the vision?

Kim believed one has to live the vision. She used the vision to check to see if their actions were aligned with the vision. "You cannot say one thing and do something differently. Down here in rural Alabama if you say one thing and do another, staff quickly question your commitment," Kim said forcefully.

> You can't say you want to have a rehabilitation facility and then not put forth money to hire staff that you need, or not provide people with the resources that they need, or make very punitive patient care policies. The decisions that you make and the actions you take must match the vision that you articulate.

Kim continued about the need to say and do the same thing.

> When we were making the transition from a very structured, tightly controlled custodial organization to a more rehabilitation-focused organization, we finally realized that the levels program, a behavioral program of which we were very proud, was being maintained solely for the benefit of the staff.

The levels program gave privileges to patients based on the behavior that staff believed was desired. Kim realized that this was a staff vision and not a consumer-based vision. "It really didn't do anything to move us closer to our consumer based vision at all." As a result, the levels program was unceremoniously discontinued.

Pablo Hernandez, a major figure in the public mental health scene for his over 40 years of contributions, was interviewed when he was superintendent of Wyoming State Hospital. When Pablo talked passionately about the organizational vision, he demonstrated how he showed the relevance of the vision to the patients and the staff. As director of a hospital whose vision included creating a more healthy environment for everyone, a part of the vision of the hospital was to become a tobacco-free, non-smoking environment.

> So our vision is that we want to create a healthier environment. We really want to create healthy people. For example, I use information about the issues around nicotine. How does nicotine affect a person with mental illness? How does nicotine interfere with the ability to assimilate some medications in your body? How do we change a "tobacco therapy" that we have used in the past, which basically consisted of "us" buying "them" cigarettes; we all smoked in front of the shelter; we all did it. How do we then change that and say we are a health care organization? We have responsibility for people that have an illness; that illness is maybe schizophrenia; maybe diabetes; maybe one of their illnesses is chronic obstructive pulmonary disease. My God, look at their hands, the marks, the staining on all of the fingers. How can we say that this person is a healthy person? So then the key is the dialogue of changing. And the key is the dialogue of getting people to say, "you know what? I really don't want to see a patient getting hurt anymore. I don't want a patient to suffer the conse-

quences of ending up with chronic obstructive pulmonary disease, or the person falling asleep in their bed and smoking. If they move to an apartment we might have a catastrophe on our hands." So it is an articulation of the vision that we go with day in and day out.

Pablo made sure people knew how important the vision of a healthier environment was to him, and tried to live a life compatible with the vision. Pablo used many ways to persuade others of the importance of the vision.

I personally have gone around the hospital grounds picking up cigarette butts in front of all the staff; in front of the patients. I need to model the importance of the vision. So modeling is something that you've got to do over and over and over again in order to create change, as a responsible and involved leader. In the early phase, when we started looking at how many cigarette butts we had everywhere, I bought one of those backpack machines, with a big sucking thing that you use to pick up leaves. I had people wearing that around campus, and it was called the "Pablo Butt Sucking Machine"; that was okay and people got the message in a funny way.

Many leaders seem to live their lives backwards in that their vision gives them an image or picture of what the results should look like, and they then create their work backwards from the outcomes implicit in the vision. Sometimes leaders seem to see the last step before they see the first step. It is the outcome, inherent in the vision, that starts to make obvious the initial steps. Leaders with vision seem to assume that the way to achieve the vision will become clear. Cynthia Barker's vision led her to purchasing a burgundy mini van; Len Stein's vision helped him to see the necessity of patients possessing their therapists' phone numbers; and Kim Ingram's vision led her to deep-six the prestigious levels program. Bob Quam's vision led him to memorialize all operational changes in policy, memos, job descriptions, formal

> Many leaders seem to live their lives backwards, in that their vision gives them an image or picture of what the results should look like, and they then create their work backwards from the outcomes implicit in the vision.

procedures, and daily walking rounds. With a clearly communicated vision sometimes the earlier steps just leap out at the organizational leadership.

Charley Curie understood the relationship between vision and outcomes. When Charley was interviewed, he was just about to step down from his position as administrator of SAMSHA (a position that Terry Cline would occupy next). Prior to that time, Charley was commissioner in Pennsylvania. He remarked:

> I think vision is the most critical aspect of leadership and if you cannot articulate a vision, you cannot articulate the outcomes of what you want to attain or what your efforts will be to accomplish these. I do not believe you can be an effective leader without a vision. When I came on board at SAMHSA, they were just arriving at what the mission/vision should be. I wanted to add a lot because I thought it was very important in order to communicate, in short hand, the appropriate message to our constituency groups and to the broader community including our customers such as Congress, the Department of Health and Human Services' Secretary, and the taxpayers who may think mental health does not affect their lives directly but are paying for it. I went to as many folks as possible to ask them what should SAMHSA do or what should be the impact of our outcomes. The constituents took on our vision and brought forth a lot of ideas to what SAMHSA should do. I did a lot of sitting down with internal staff, in terms of learning about SAMHSA, and to keep an eye on what was happening in terms of accomplishments. I also took into consideration the years of listening to consumers in Pennsylvania.

Charley reflected further on the consistencies he heard in the remarks from consumers and their families.

> When I listened to what outcomes people with mental illnesses or their families wanted for their loved ones it always seemed to come down to the same things. They wanted to have a meaningful life in the community, but their illness kept getting in the way of them feeling as though they were fully participating. There was also this constant theme of feeling marginalized because of discrimination that was overt and insidious. But, in any case, it is the

outcomes of care that are most important, and as leaders, we need to figure out how best to get to these outcomes. If the vision of the leadership is not rooted in what the people whom we are serving want, the vision is going to be irrelevant coming out of the chute. The vision needs to be owned by all and rooted in feedback.

Similar to this book, Charley differentiated between vision and mission, believing that "mission is what you focus on in order to achieve your vision. Vision comes first, guides your ultimate outcome and drives your mission statement."

Perhaps one of the most visible city and state mental health directors during the late 1970s through the early 1990s was Richard Surles. Richard was interviewed shortly after his departure as commissioner of mental health for the state of New York, and then again a number of years later. Prior to being commissioner in New York State, he had directed mental health services in the state of Vermont and the city of Philadelphia. In each setting, he brought direction and energy to the mental health organizations. Richard maintained that a leader's vision is especially important in times of cost cutting and organizational crisis. While it might seem, at first blush, that vision is most critical when the organization is growing, an organization under stress needs vision even more. Cutting staff and programs is intolerable without a vision toward which the organization is moving. With vision, the organizational contraction choices make some sense. Without vision, the cost cutting is typically "across the board," with no differentiation relevant to vision. The cost cutting exercise seems mindless and out of control. While few organizations desire reductions, they can only be tolerable when they are consistent with the organization's vision. According to Richard, "during budget cutting, the vision became critical in deciding what to cut and what to even grow."

Carlos Brandenburg from Nevada amplified on the point made by Richard Surles.

The state went through a very bad financial crisis. We lost a lot of our services. But it also gave me the opportunity to get rid of some sacred cows that were being funded by folks that thought they were doing well, but the programs did not have any outcomes. They were programs that weren't efficient, weren't effective. So it allowed me to basically get rid of those programs and start developing programs that had clear visions, that had good outcomes, good indicators.

It appears that there is no one way to develop and communicate a vision. Leaders develop their own vision with their staff in their own way, sometimes intellectually, sometimes intuitively, and sometimes emotionally. Tom Lane communicated the vision emotionally.

Tom Lane was the vice president of Recovery Support and Forensics Services at New Horizon's Community Mental Health Center in Florida when he was interviewed. Consistent with the tasks outlined in principle 1, Tom emphasized the importance of a shared vision, communicated clearly and repeatedly, in a way that is relevant to the organization's consumers and is potent enough to shape the organization's future. He spoke about the vision of recovery from severe mental illnesses in a compelling way.

> As a person living with a psychiatric disability, in a leadership role in an organization, I found the most powerful way to communicate the vision I hoped others would share was to share my own experiences of recovery. I self-disclose as a person who lives well with bipolar disorder and a co-occurring disorder.

Tom believed that he could build awareness of the fact that recovery was possible and as a result build a climate of hope within the organization by sharing his personal story.

> I talked about what it was like to be on an inpatient unit and be ignored while standing at the nursing station. I talked about the difference it made when a mental health technician working the graveyard shift, spent time talking with me, encouraging me— telling me I would get better, that I was not my illness. I talked about my own recovery in senior management meetings, with other division leaders, with clinical staff on the inpatient units, and with staff in our screening and assessment area. I shared my story with staff working in the business office, with staff working in medical records, with MIS employees, and with staff who work in the facilities department.

Sometimes it is not the current leader who creates the vision; and sometimes the leader patiently lets the vision emerge and evolve. In Mike Hogan's situation in Ohio, the vision began to emerge from former leaders and current staff. The leader may be needed to recognize and support the existence of an already created vision or one that comes from the suggestions of the staff. Nevertheless, it is the leader's job to make sure that the vision is communicated and shared by all within the organization. The leader is the most effective spokesperson for the vision.

> Sometimes it is not the current leader who creates the vision; and sometimes the leader patiently lets the vision emerge and evolve...Nevertheless, it is the leader's job to make sure that the vision is communicated and shared by all within the organization.

When Richard Surles first assumed leadership of the New York State mental health system, he believed he had to be patient and not come in too early with a vision, but rather let it develop. This perspective is somewhat similar to Hogan's actions in Ohio, in not wanting to be singularly intrusive. In Hogan's case, there was an emphasis on collaboration in visioning, while in Surles' case, he made sure time was taken for the vision to develop. In the interview, Surles remarked that, "of all the leadership principles, principle one was hands down the most difficult thing to do." One must be willing to be patient, and to communicate the vision in a way that doesn't devalue what others are doing now or were doing in the past. In order to ensure that devaluing didn't occur, his message to his staff was:

> I don't want to think about the way things are today; let's think about the way we want them to be two or three years from now; let's have a discussion about the future, realizing that we need to make a transformation. We only need to go back and look at our current strategies and activities in light of where we want to be three years from now.

Richard Surles' emphasis on the importance of vision was certainly recognized by his staff. Sandy Forquer, one time a deputy commissioner in New York State with Richard Surles, reminisced in her interview. "I can't say enough about the importance of communicating a clear vision. The mentor who taught me that was

Richard Surles." When Sandy was interviewed she was head of the Colorado Health Network, which was run by Options, a private, for-profit managed care firm.

> Principle 1 is a most important principle. In Colorado, our vision led to a system that valued rehabilitation and recovery, and gave consumers a larger role in designing the system. We used retreats and monthly partnership meetings to constantly revisit the vision.

Principled leaders can help the vision grow in clarity and power over time. Bennis (1989) maintains that there are three sources from which a leader draws when developing a vision: the past, present, and future. From the past, one can identify analogies and precedents from which to draw. The present provides an approximation of the resources that will go into creating the work of future toward which the vision is directed. Future predictions of what to expect are unfortunately all too commonplace—and typically wrong. Interestingly, however, by crafting an influential vision, the leader can shape the future in which the vision exists. Through their shared vision, leaders are, in fact, designing the future. It is critical that the vision be capable of being understood because when staff can understand and agree with the vision, then they become empowered to advance that vision. Staff realize that their tasks that are consistent with the vision will be valued by the leader and the organization.

> It is critical that the vision be capable of being understood because when staff can understand and agree with the vision, then they become empowered to advance that vision.

Pablo Hernandez' many leadership experiences in the mental health system taught him the importance of patience as staff gradually understood the importance and relevance of the vision to them.

> I have needed to be extremely cautious in using this visionary process so to not to be too pushy that I scare people off. The articulation of the vision needs to take place within a very well planned, easy to understand, and thoughtful process that will describe almost a road map of how we will get there. This takes time, and the time frame needs to be cautiously balanced so oth-

ers can find their own comfort zone and come to accept the vision within their comfort zone. It cannot just be the vision of the leader. It has to be a composite of how every one else thinks and feels about it, and assure that the other individuals who are going to be participants in creating that future can really see where things will be going; looking and accepting how we want the future to be. One of the best predictors of the future is to be able to articulate a vision. Not to create it completely on my own, but to articulate it well enough so that staff can say, "Oh, I got it." I never lambaste what others have done in the past or want in the future because I think that's when my ideas of a vision can be counter-productive; when a leader begins to say things like, "we must change everything all around; nothing has worked; nothing was of value." That kind of talk becomes an obstruction. This kind of criticism does not mobilize people in the right way. It places people on the defense, and then from there, it begins to be destructive. So if we were going to say we will have a vision of recovery, then we present this first by articulating that recovery comes in many different glasses; comes in many different shapes and comes in many different forms.

Nanus (1992) also has talked about what a vision can do. His comments are very compatible with what a vision in a mental health organization can do. A vision establishes a pride in the organization; it inspires staff; it lets people know what the organization stands for; it builds to the future; it creates meaning in the workers' lives. Furthermore, Nanus states that an organizational vision sets a standard of excellence that reflects high ideals, describes the purpose and direction of the organization, and encourages commitment. Bennis (1989) remarks how a shared vision helps staff figure out their own roles in the organization as well as the larger society. When individuals are proud of the vision of the organization in which they work, it confers status on them outside the workplace.

Peter Senge (2006) notes that if any one issue has been able to move successful organizations forward it is a "shared picture of the future [they] seek to create" (p. 9). Senge also notes that he is unaware of any organization that has achieved greatness without goals, values, and a vision statement that is ingrained in the work-force. Senge believes that when there is a viable shared vision, as opposed to the usual superficial vision statement, that people in the organization excel, learn, and grow through internal motiva-tions, rather than just being told to change.

One thing about creating a vision seems clear. A leader cannot demand that a vision be followed, and at the same time have a vision that creates energy or empowerment. The leader must be skilled in persuading others of the potency of the vision—for the organization and for themselves. It must be seen by the leaders' followers as the right vision at the right time. The leader needs to use the right stories and/or metaphors that appeal to his or her fol-lowers' reason and emotion. Most of all, the vision must feel right to the people who will be making it come alive.

The birth of a vision cannot be pushed and shoved on to peo-ple. Rather, just like the birth of the blues, it must be "nursed and rehearsed." Then, once you hear the splendid harmonizing, you cannot get the vision out of your experience.

2

Leaders centralize by mission and decentralize by operations.

- The leader uses the mission to focus the entire organization on how the organization can benefit its consumers.

- The leader identifies the separate processes that need operational leadership.

- The leader gives responsibility and authority to the operational staff.

- The leader encourages staff to process relevant information themselves.

- The leader encourages staff to participate in the decision making.

- The leader manages at a more macro than micro level.

- The leaders at the mission level serve as role models for leaders at the operational level.

- The leader identifies the different outcomes of the different units of the organization.

- The leader discerns what is required and takes those actions that are sufficient and feasible for the success of the organization.

- The leader ensures that staff understand that all operational outcomes are critical to the organization's mission.

- The leader understands that all procedures, no matter how small, reflect on the mission.

- The leader encourages communication between different levels of the organizational chart.

Leaders centralize by mission and decentralize by operations.

Vision is a necessary but not sufficient condition of leadership.

—William A. Anthony

The vision captures the future destination of the organization. However, the train will never leave the station for the vision destination if the organization lacks a mission and a way to implement the mission. Perhaps the most pathetic situation is an organization with an exciting vision and no understanding of how to pursue it.

A vision is not a mission. While the vision gives you an image of the future, the mission speaks to what the organization must do right now—its primary purpose. The mission focuses the entire organization—its energy, its intellectual resources, and its passion on those activities that need to be done in order for the consumer to realize the benefits of receiving services from the organization.

Chapters 1, 2, and 3 of *Principled Leadership* focus on four important organizational concepts: vision (chapter 1); mission and operations (chapter 2); and values (chapter 3).

For the principled leader these concepts are critically interrelated and require alignment and congruence. A *vision* tells what future the organization is trying to create. The *mission* defines what role the organization has in creating that future. *Operations* describe the daily, priority activities that take place in the organization to accomplish the mission. The *values* provide the template that guides the organizational decision making that directs the daily operations.

An excellent example of how a leader attempts to align vision, mission, operations, and values was provided by Kathy Muscari. When Kathy was interviewed, she was a leader in the West Virginia Mental Health Consumers' Association and the director of CONTAC, the Consumer Organization and Networking Technical Assistance Center. Kathy first described the vision and the organization's role in moving the field closer to the vision.

> The vision of the West Virginia Mental Health Consumers' Association (WVMHCA) has been to create a consumer-driven behavioral health system. When that became the vision years ago, it seemed like a distant dream. Today, it has become a very real possibility. The mission of our organization is to work toward this vision through developing services and supports that promote education and training, build strong peer networks, and assist with independent living in the community.

Kathy continued on to portray how they organized their separate processes toward that mission.

> When I accepted a leadership position at WVMHCA, I knew, from my background in nonprofit management, our organization would benefit from re-looking at its authoritative organizational structure. Through a series of team meetings, we developed a flattened hierarchy that depicted operational components of the organization. These were in areas of living, learning, working, and connecting. We developed corresponding job descriptions for directors of housing, education and training, and resource drop-in centers. Once a month, representatives from these different components now meet for information-sharing and planning. In the time between meetings, they run their particular divisions through teamwork and field-based knowledge.

Next Kathy illustrated how the communications that are needed to make the organization work are guided by the mission and values (Further information on the key values of the organization are provided by Kathy in chapter 3.)

> Decisions are made based upon our mission and values. Instead of the board of directors or CEO being at the top of our organiza-

tional chart, it is the consumers of the state of West Virginia. Everyone has a key role in the success of our organization and takes pride in his or her efforts. There is a management coordinating unit that is comprised of division directors. This unit also acts as a team and role models organizational values and mission support. It assures that there is common understanding of roles and responsibilities as well as mutually prepared work plans for each program. We capture outcome data. To help make operations effective and communication open across the organizational structure, we have invested in information technology and staff development and training. I'm pleased to be part of a learning organization that has interesting programs, projects, and services. Even so, as the old saying goes, WVMHCA's whole is bigger than its parts. There is magic when the organization hums.

The focus of this particular chapter is how the leader makes the operations "hum" (to use Kathy Muscari's term) by centralizing by mission and decentralizing by operations. Gene Johnson provided an excellent example of how the evolution of META's mission statement clarified META's role in pursuing a recovery vision.

When I founded META Services in 1990, the idea was to create service alternatives. In the beginning the name META stood for Maricopa East Treatment Alternatives. I organized a board of directors and was awarded our first contract to provide "crisis stabilization services" in a 10-bed facility that was a converted house. It seemed like the perfect alternative, and many of the people we served found it much more comforting to be at META than to be confined in a hospital. Around this experience we developed our mission statement, "to be the premiere provider of crisis stabilization services." This mission—stabilization—really did guide the development of our services. In the early 90s, we didn't know much about recovery for people labeled with "serious mental illnesses," and I thought stabilization was something to celebrate. But all the while, there was this nagging feeling of discomfort and dissatisfaction. Earlier in my career, I had developed and managed substance abuse services and knew that people with addiction could recover. I hoped the same could be true for the people we

were serving who had been diagnosed with serious mental illnesses. Without really knowing recovery could be possible, I created
the byline "the recovery alternative." Our mission was stabilization, so I didn't talk about "the recovery alternative" much, but
our literature said that's what we were, and I think that kept the
dream alive.

Gene spoke fervently about how the organizational mission
evolved as their vision became clearer.

One day I came across Mary Ellen Copeland and the Wellness
Recovery Action Plan. I was excited to hear that there was a way
that people could develop a program of self-help to manage,
reduce, and eliminate psychiatric symptoms. I
went to Vermont and learned to be a WRAP
facilitator. I began to learn about recovery and
read everything I could find, and attended just
about every conference there was, having anything to do with recovery. I listened to Bill
Anthony, Pat Deegan, Dan Fischer, Judi Chamberlin, and many others, and slowly became convinced that our
mission of stabilization not only failed to inspire hope, but was
way too small. My organization had a mission that exemplified
low expectations. I couldn't live with that. I wanted to create a
bigger and better future. So, I convened all our META leadership
and had a day-long "think" about who we were and who we
wanted to be. That day, in 2000, we created a new mission statement: To create opportunities and environments that empower
people to recover, to succeed in accomplishing their goals, and to
reconnect to themselves, others, and meaning and purpose in life.
Wow! That was a huge leap for us. We didn't know what would
show up by moving from stabilization to recovery, but we all
chose the journey.

> My organization had a
> mission that exemplified low
> expectations. I couldn't live
> with that. I wanted to create
> a bigger and better future.

Gene had moved from embracing the recovery vision to identifying the compatible mission—or the role META would play in
working toward the vision.

Since that day in 2000, every day I communicate our purpose
through the mission statement. On the first day of employment in

our "new hire celebration," I greet each new employee and talk about our mission; who we are, what we believe in, and what our purpose is. I describe our values and invite new employees to contribute. I ask each new employee to memorize our mission statement and bring it with them each morning they come to work. Within 90 days of hire, each employee has to complete a 6-class, 12-hour recovery training. I deliver the second class, Organizational Recovery.

I ask the new employees to recite our mission statement. A few can and I applaud them. Then we take time to all learn it together. But, with each word, I explain our intent. For example, it starts with "To create...." We talk about how together we get to create the future. It is up to us. We discuss how we will make our future great. We talk about what we are creating: "opportunities and environments." And that it's the person's job to recover. We discuss all the recovery opportunities we have created and think about those we might want to create. We talk about what a recovery environment is like and discuss my view of an "empowered organization."

Once a week we have "Morning Meeting" with all of our leadership. Thirty five of us get together for a time of sharing and inspiration. At that meeting, I'll ask everyone to recite together our mission statement. I ask leadership to have their team recite our mission statement in their meetings. At Peer Employment Training graduations and other graduations in our Recovery Education Center, I'll share our mission statement. Constantly and continuously I present and represent our recovery purpose through our mission statement.

Like Gene, Mary Alice Brown is definitely a leader with a mission, and an operation designed to achieve the mission. When Mary Alice Brown was interviewed, she was the executive director of Laurel Hill Center, a nonprofit rehabilitation agency located in Eugene, Oregon. Mary Alice was Laurel Hill's first director in 1972, when Laurel Hill started as a drop-in social club for patients released from the state hospital and quickly blossomed into a program offering vocational, housing, and social programs (Brown &

Basel, 1989). The mission of the organization always has been clear. When Mary Alice was interviewed, the mission was to help people make choices and to acquire the skills and supports that increase their self reliance and ability to live and work in the community. Mary Alice used the mission to allow new initiatives to emerge that were consistent with the mission. As a matter of fact, when opportunities arose that were consistent with the mission, her staff believed that they would find a way to implement the operational requirements as long as the new initiative was consistent with their mission.

Laurel Hill's initiation of the supported housing program is an example. When the idea of supported housing first was being discussed in the literature, Laurel Hill already had begun one of the first supported housing programs in the country (Brown & Wheeler, 1990). While Laurel Hill's supported housing program, initiated in 1981, met with early success, skeptics in the mental health system felt that the people receiving supported housing services were not really "severely mentally ill" and that this type of intervention would not work with a population that was most disabled. At about this time, the state had designated a group of folks as "most difficult to serve" by virtue of their commitment to the state hospital at least twice in the last three years and had earmarked funding for supported housing for this group of people. After demonstrating the success of this program (Brown, Ridgeway, Anthony & Rogers, 1991), when another opportunity arose due to additional state hospital downsizing, the leadership once again seized this moment and sought to combine mental health and vocational rehabilitation state funding to develop a combined supported housing and supported work initiative for people transitioning out of the hospital. This initiative was needed because the state division of vocational rehabilitation had incorrectly assumed that people would move out of long term hospitalization into employment in a matter of months. The successful results of this combined housing and vocational program were

> When opportunities arose that were consistent with the mission…staff believed that they would find a way to implement the operational requirements as long as the new initiative was consistent with their mission.

evaluated and disseminated to the field (Anthony, Brown, Rogers, & Derringer, 1999).

Mary Alice remarked that, "we are constantly doing new things that we have never done before." When the organization takes on these new initiatives, Mary Alice puts different people in charge of these operations to provide the leadership to these separate programs. She gives the operational leadership the responsibility and authority to "make the program work." While the outcomes of a housing program and a vocational program are obviously very different, each operational leader knows exactly toward what organizational goals they are working and how each ties into the mission.

As new opportunities emerge that are consistent with the overall organizational mission, Mary Alice states that she can count on her staff saying, "I wonder if we can do this. Let's learn more about this." An outstanding example was their bidding on and winning the Oregon state contract for producing eye glasses for people on medical assistance. Even though they had never attempted this business and had virtually no experience, they learned how to do it and won the state contract to make eye glasses. The making of eyeglasses is a marketable skill for their people to learn and a source of revenue that can support other less funded programs in the organization. This operation is so impressive you would swear you were at a major eyeglass retailer when you enter this component of the program.

> As new opportunities emerge that are consistent with the overall organizational mission… she can count on her staff saying, "I wonder if we can do this. Let's learn more about this."

The concept of reengineering (Hammer & Champy, 1993) became popular in the 1990s because leaders had overmanaged the various processes that comprised their businesses. Old ideas, such as the division of labor, the need for elaborate controls on that labor, and the resulting managerial hierarchy created organizations that were overmanaged and underled. As the management task became more complicated and difficult, the processes became more fragmented from one another, and seemingly, more managers were needed to keep the organization from unraveling.

In the field of mental health, and way ahead of the reengineering curve, were people like Len Stein and his colleagues in Wisconsin (first mentioned in chapter 1), who knit the process of helping people with severe mental illnesses back together again through the forerunner of what is now called Assertive Community Treatment (ACT). The process of helping someone realize the vision of being treated in the community was accomplished by doing away with the middle management structure of a hospital and developing a community team that worked collaboratively towards the mission of helping people live their lives in the community. Consistent with reengineering, Len Stein organized work around a process.

In the language of reengineering, a process is a collection of activities that takes one or more kinds of input and creates an output that is of value to the customer. These processes or operations are needed when different types of consumer outcomes are attempted. Stated most simply, in the field of mental health, when the outcome is improved role functioning for consumers, the service delivery process includes rehabilitation. When the consumer outcome is symptom relief, the service delivery process includes treatment. Table 3 provides an example of different consumer outcomes and the name of the service delivery process that is specifically focused on that outcome.

> In the field of mental health, when the outcome is improved role functioning for consumers, the service delivery process includes rehabilitation. When the consumer outcome is symptom relief, the service delivery process includes treatment.

Even within these broad consumer outcomes on which the operations or processes of mental health services are focused, there may be further separations of the process. For example, in organizations such as Laurel Hill, which provide psychiatric rehabilitation services (toward the outcome of improved role functioning), there may be variations of the psychiatric rehabilitation process when the role outcome is vocational than when the role outcome is residential. In this example, the content of what a practitioner needs to know is different, perhaps the speed of the process is different, and the outcome environment is certainly different. In some psychiatric rehabilitation organizations, for example, the residential and

**Table 3. Unique Service Processes, Descriptions, and Outcomes—
Essential Client Services in a Recovery-Oriented System**

Service Process	Description of Service Process	Consumer Outcome
Treatment	Alleviating symptoms and distress	Symptom relief
Crisis intervention	Controlling and resolving critical or dangerous problems	Personal safety assured
Case management	Obtaining the services person needs and wants	Services accessed
Rehabilitation	Developing peoples' skills and supports related to their goals	Role functioning
Enrichment	Engaging people in fulfilling and satisfying activities	Self-development
Rights protection	Advocating to uphold persons' rights	Equal opportunity
Basic support	Providing the people, places, and things individuals need to survive (e.g., shelter, meals, health care)	Personal survival assured
Self-help	Exercising a voice and a choice in one's life	Empowerment
Wellness/ Prevention	Promoting healthy lifestyles	Health status improved

Adapted from: Cohen, M., Cohen, B., Nemec, P., Farkas, M. & Forbess, R. (1988). *Training technology: Case management.* Boston: Boston University, Center for Psychiatric Rehabilitation.

vocational operations may be done by the same person or team of persons, while in other organizations, they may be organized into separate processes.

These separate processes or operations must be consistent with the organization's mission, which ultimately reflects the organization's overall vision. Of major importance to the concept of effective leadership, these separate operations must not only be managed, they must be led. The goals of each operational process become, in essence, the mission of the leader of that operation. It is around these operational goals or operational missions that the work of the organization is accomplished in a way that the organizational mission is realized.

King Davis spoke directly to the importance of connecting each person's activities to the organization's vision and mission. When King was interviewed, he was executive director of the Hogg Foundation in Austin Texas, prior to that, he served as commissioner of Virginia's Department of Mental Health. King said:

> The goals of each operational process become, in essence, the mission of the leader of that operation.

I've used the Hogg mission and the vision statements to centralize the mission and decentralize the operations. I have encouraged my entire group of managers to take responsibility for the operations. I have tried as much as possible to step back, once the vision and the mission were clear, to allow the various unit directors and each of the staff members to carry out the specific operations that are attached to that mission without my having to basically, on a day-to-day basis, assume overall responsibility for the specific things that go on in the organization.

Kathryn Power was interviewed when she was director of the Center for Mental Health Services (CMHS), a division of the Substance Abuse and Mental Health Services Administration, where Charley Curie and then Terry Cline were the administrators. Prior to leading CMHS, Kathryn had many other leadership positions, including commissioner of Department of Mental Health in Rhode Island.

Under Kathryn's leadership, CMHS was charged to take a leadership role in helping state systems transform themselves into a vision consistent with recovery, as described in the report of the President's New Freedom Commission (2003). When she took this federal position, she knew that a major responsibility of her leadership was to get the directors of all the operational programs within CMHS on board with this transformational mission.

Kathryn stated, in her interview, how much the individual processes at CMHS needed to change if the transformation mission was to be realized.

First and foremost I think transformation really involves an internal shift; that the transformation of this country's mental health care delivery system requires a shift of perspective; a shift of perception; and a shift from what is current reality to another kind of order. It takes an enormous amount of time and energy and effort for people to realize that the old federal bureaucratic thinking around the way things should be done, while it is not bad or good, needs to change. While staff might say "this is the way we've always done it," or "this is the way we've always defined mental health systems," or "this is the way we've always treated state authorities," or "this is the way grantees have always done it," now CMHS staff must embrace the concept of transformative change.

So we have, since I've been at CMHS, spent a lot of time having brown bag discussions about transformation and creating libraries so people could read about transformation in mental health and in other organizations. We've had a transformation university going almost two years; this is our internal educational program where we have selective training on different topics. For example, what we found at CMHS was that the homelessness program was known about by the people in the homelessness program, but not necessarily by the other program people. As such, we found that we needed to do a lot of cross-fertilization across all the CMHS divisions just to set the stage for people to begin to think how their work, individually, had applicability to transformation. So there's a lot of internal education, internal exposure, and internal discussion around the concept of transformation that's going on at CMHS and has been going on for some time.

Kathryn also extended the principle of getting organizational operations aligned with the CMHS mission to other federal agencies, outside of her control. Kathryn spoke about working with SAMHSA's federal partners, in other federal agencies, to understand the CMHS mission.

We knew that the mental health system was no longer, and probably never was, the sole owner of the issues related to getting appropriate mental health and substance abuse care to individuals. So, in coming together, the federal partners became sort of the second level of transformational work, and that is still on-going. Basically the process that we've used primarily was simply professional outreach in a personal manner to those individuals at my level across the federal government. We asked them, "We would like to find out what you think about transformation. We'd like to find out what you think you can do in terms of our goals and objectives, about the New Freedom Commission Report; let's start a dialogue." And, I think what has grown from that is a very solid, very consultative collaboration across the federal government that is working toward transformation of the mental health system.

In Richard Surles' work as commissioner of mental health in New York State, he believed strongly in giving authority and responsibility to operational staff to try new initiatives. They were encouraged to make decisions. His strong direction to them was, "I'll support you as long as you are right." In other words, he wouldn't tell them exactly what to do, but felt that it must be consistent with the mission and values. Richard knew that while some operational leaders were pleased with this directive, others were para-lyzed by the responsibility. Some wanted to be told exactly how to do it. Of course by demonstrating their incapacity to lead in an operation centralized by mission and decentralized by operations, these would-be operational leaders were demonstrating their lack of leadership skills.

> By demonstrating their incapacity to lead in an operation centralized by mission and decentralized by operations, these would-be operational leaders were demonstrating their lack of leadership skills.

In Oklahoma, before he became SAMHSA director, Terry Cline gave his program leaders responsibility and authority to instill various improvements in their processes that were consistent with their state's mission. Terry noted:

One services program implemented basically an open door policy, open access for people needing services. They made a commit-ment that when somebody calls and says they want to come in, they will free up their resources to make sure that person gets served right then and there. What this provider found was, that in general, there was enough flexibility in schedules due to no-shows or people who had scheduled paper work time that walk-ins could be handled. They also found that the "show-up rate" was much higher for these individuals who were walk-ins, as they were getting the people at a high point in their own personal motivation to get help. And finally, that this new system actually saved time in the long run because you didn't schedule an appointment for two weeks later and then have a clinician and a clerk sitting there waiting for somebody to come in, only to be disappointed because they no-showed two weeks later or six weeks later, depending on how long a waiting list might be. So there's been a much lower rate of no-shows and a higher rate of shows for first appointment and then engagement and follow up as a result of that.

Another example is that we had a pretty in-depth admission process that included proving income eligibility; this process had state documentation requirements that mandated proof that a person was within 200% of the federal poverty level. You know, that's a great rapport builder! "Do you have your work pay stub?" "Do you have a tax form?" "Do you have a checkbook; anything that will help us figure that out?" Meanwhile, not literally, but figuratively, these folks are "bleeding for help," and then we wonder why they don't come back for a second visit? So for this select group, we completely eliminated the income eligibility requirements. We're still examining that data, but what we believe to be true is that the majority of people are eligible anyway, so why alienate 95% of the people for that 5%? And if we eventually think that we are overlooking too many people who can pay something for services, we can revisit the income issue in the third session, after we have built some rapport and have some buy-in.

When Larry Miller was interviewed, he was the medical director in the mental health department in Arkansas. Prior to that he was medical director at the Arkansas State Hospital. Larry emphasized the importance of giving responsibility and authority to staff who managed certain processes. He used, as an example, his operational decentralization during Arkansas State Hospital's seclusion/restraint (S/R) reduction planning. Larry said:

I delegated a lot of operational kinds of things to staff. We had about six operational categories on our S/R reduction plan and a leader for each. The leaders would choose staff to work in their group, and they could expand the group in terms of membership or scope as long as it stayed within our basic vision. I wanted staff to take the lead and run with it as long as it made some sense; they took the primary responsibility on themselves, with some help now and again. I'm really very proud of the work they did in terms of seclusion and restraint. It became their project, and they continue to move it along even though I am no longer at the hospital.

Also, Larry mentioned that in another project initiative, he tried to serve as a role model for those at the operational level by actually managing one of the priority processes himself.

Leaders at the higher organizational levels understand that their job is to make sure that the leaders at the operational level act in accordance with the mission of the organization. These leaders at the executive level also understand that if the organization itself is going to succeed, then the leaders at the operational level cannot be micromanaged. No matter what level of the organization chart, executive leaders are spokespersons and coaches. But they are not managers of someone else's operation unless there is a crisis. Richard Surles' directive that he would support his operational leaders "as long as you are right," prevented him from getting sucked into managing his staff's operation.

> Leaders at the executive level also understand that if the organization itself is going to succeed, then the leaders at the operational level cannot be micromanaged.

As described by Raul Almazar, CEO of Elgin State Hospital in Illinois, the particular mission of their organization around which their operations revolved turned out to be an old mission.

When we first started working on revising our mission, we added in stuff about using evidence-based care and avoiding coercion, etc. Then, last January, we returned to our mission of 1872. That mission was right, even back then. We just did not see it. Our mission now says, "We provide treatment for the relief and restoration of the people we serve so that they may find health and happiness again." Powerful. We went through all of the buzz words until someone said, 'what about the old plaque on the wall" and we all related immediately to that.

Raul went on to describe how decentralization around that mission began to take hold, and how this "decentralizing" has made his job easier.

The whole focus of decentralization and making things happen at the local unit level became clearer to us in the last few years. I hold a hospital executive committee meeting for two hours once a month. Before decentralization began, there was never enough time, so many issues to discuss and decisions to make at this senior level. But after I handed off many of these daily decisions, we soon realized we had nothing to talk about. My hospital executive committee was now spending only 30 minutes, on average, in these meetings. When we realized this change, we looked at it closely and what became apparent was that the people on the units had become empowered, especially through the daily community meetings. Both in community meetings and individually, they had become empowered to make decisions either through negotiating, through email, or by picking up the phone to ask for consultation to help in the decisions they wanted to make; this shifted the power to them. Now we no longer have so many decisions to make in executive committee. My work has become so much easier. In my all-staff meeting this morning, one person said to me, "you know, we've seen you more lately," and they were right. I have more time to get around. I have fewer crises to put out. It is quite clear to leadership that power, in this hospital, has been decentralized."

Organizational leaders can clear the path for the operational leaders, but they cannot travel the path. They show interest, they ask questions, they make suggestions, they may take actions at critical times, they inspire, they reinforce the vision and the organization's mission—but they are careful to let effective operational leaders lead. They are role models for the leadership at the oper-

> Organizational leaders can clear the path for the operational leaders, but they cannot travel the path.

ations' level, just as the operational leaders are role models for their own staff. As designated leaders at the highest levels of the organization, they personify the vision and model the mission, but they do not lead where others can. Leaders beget leaders—like acorns beget oaks.

Elizabeth Childs was interviewed when she was commissioner of the Department of Mental Health in Massachusetts. She described how important it was to give responsibility and authority to the operational staff, and to manage her staff at a macro rather than a micro level. Elizabeth stated:

> I have exemplary staff and am quite blessed with that. I try not to be a micromanager, but I am also not afraid to get my hands dirty. I mean if there's a big problem, I will dig in and help out and try to help carry some of the load. I think my management team has come to a shared vision, and I think you can only manage a larger organization if you have consensus on a vision, and you make sure that people buy into that vision. Then you must let them go and do the implementation because they're closer to it and know how to do it in ways that I never could. Some issues I have realized I cannot even get involved with, without mucking them up, even with best intentions. So for some issues I ask a senior staff person to run point on this; I need you to make this work.

> The less I have to touch operationally the better it works, and when I touch it operationally it usually indicates that we've got some bigger systemic problem that I need to address that I haven't addressed yet.

In a way, the less I have to touch operationally, the better it works, and when I touch it operationally, it usually indicates that we've got some bigger systemic problem that I need to address that I haven't addressed yet. If we are working from the organizational vision, the expectations are clear and the accountability is clear, it's clear who's running this initiative and I have good people in there doing it; these are the key ingredients, and I shouldn't have to be directly involved in the operation. So when I get involved in the operation, it usually is a signal to me that one of those things is not happening. I either haven't deployed enough resources, have not been clear about expectations, or whoever is working on the project doesn't have the vision down, they don't get it. Or maybe I choose the wrong people, or I've got the right people but they don't have the right support. It can be a whole combination of things. It's always striking to me how I have great relationships with my fellow commissioners and other agency heads here in Massachusetts. We can agree on a course of action or a project that we're going to do together, but then it works best if we turn the operations over to our strong senior team.

Elizabeth elaborated on this principle with respect to the importance of communication with her staff so that there is staff understanding and involvement in the decision making process.

I meet with my senior team regularly, not as much as I would like, but I think I meet with my senior team probably more than most leaders. I meet one-on-one at least every other week. I try to meet weekly with my most senior people, at least my four deputy commissioners, but I even meet one level below that with my assistant commissioners. I meet with them at least once a month or every other week.

I also have two weekly team meetings. One weekly team meeting with my first level down and my second level down; my deputies and my assistants and that's a meeting of about 12 people. It's a big meeting and we focus on operational implementation issues, complexities and resolutions. Then my other weekly meeting is my most senior team, my director's board, and there are eight of us in that team, and I run that meeting. It is very focused on strategic thinking and where we are going with the policy decisions.

Elizabeth also described how separate processes contribute to the overall intent of the organization.

Coming in as a new leader of an organization, I initiated the senior leadership's development of a strategic plan and built it in the context of what was happening at the federal level with the New Freedom Commission and the IOM reports on quality. We had three top strategic priorities. We are driving them forward, and we've made tremendous progress on one of them actually. By next month I think I will secure all the funding to replace two aging state hospitals with a new state hospital. That's not just a capital project; in order to do that we had to significantly improve our operations in our inpatient settings to prove we could do better work with one new hospital, instead of two very aged ones. We had to dramatically increase our community support, community services, and over the last two years, we infused another $20 million into our community. Someday, hopefully, this will be the only hospital we have. It would be great if we could get down to having just that one hospital. It will be the single largest capital project in Massachusetts, other than the highway project. And that's an incredible accomplishment here.

In organizations that attempt to promote leadership at all levels, the organizational structure becomes less hierarchical. Organizational charts are less important because they change regularly. Processes that no longer make sense are discarded or changed. New leaders for new or modified processes emerge constantly. People communicate between levels on the organizational chart.

When Larry Kohn was first interviewed several years ago, he was director of the services division of the Center for Psychiatric Rehabilitation. The services division demonstrated the value of psychiatric rehabilitation services provided within the context of a research and training center on a university campus. It was a laboratory for the university researchers and educators to test out what they were learning, and a natural and non-traditional setting (a college campus) for people with psychiatric disabilities to participate in their rehabilitation. Furthermore, the presence of a services division in a research and training center kept the center from becoming an ivory tower; in one sense, it kept the academics humble. When Larry Kohn heard about a leader who was chastised for discussing ideas with someone in a large organization who was at a higher level on the organizational chart, Larry was incredulous.

> In organizations that attempt to promote leadership at all levels, the organizational structure becomes less hierarchical. Organizational charts are less important because they change regularly.

It is just another example of how fidelity to an organizational chart can squash good ideas. That would never happen in the Center's service division because we see the organizational chart as a requirement by others who expect such a tool. But to us, it might be a tool that hinders more work than it helps.

In essence, the organizational chart is too static to reflect what is really going on. It is the organization's existence, and not the existence of the organizational chart, that allows the vision and mission to exert their influence. No matter how negative some might feel about organizations, the bottom line is that in order for visions and missions to be approximated, there needs to be an organization. Leaders are more influential when they have an institution or organizational base. In mental health, it is difficult for leaders to exert their influence solely on the basis of their ideas. It is almost incumbent upon a leader or the leaders they beget to use or develop some type of organizational structure and operational processes.

> It is the organization's existence, and not the existence of the organizational chart, that allows the vision and mission to exert their influence.

In Linda Rosenberg's situation, her organization was immense, and certainly had the possibility of being unwieldy due to its size and scope. Linda Rosenberg was interviewed when she was executive director of the National Council of Community Behavioral Healthcare (NCCBH). Prior to that position, she had served in many leadership positions in New York State, the most recent being the senior deputy commissioner. NCCBH is a large nationwide organization; at the time of her interview it had 1,300 organizational members and 45 state associations. The NCCBH advocates for people who need mental health and substance abuse treatment to ensure that they have access to treatment of the highest quality. Linda recounted a number of initiatives that they had going at any one time, ranging from the integration of mental health and physical health care, to smoking cessation programs, to workforce retention planning. NCCBH has a board with numerous committees. Linda said the only way to make the organization function effectively in all these many initiatives was to communicate—not try to manage everything.

> Our listserve is really active and timely, and it is the place where people interact around issues of importance to them. I write a monthly letter to members that often will focus on a specific issue. We also have a theme-based newsletter we do. We do a technical

assistance newsletter on funding opportunities; we do a weekly policy update—all of this by e-mail, so we have a very vibrant virtual community we're trying to create. We also arrange monthly conference calls around these topics. We have a very large annual conference; 1,500 to 2,000 members will be there, as well as other people. So we try as much as we can to always to be communicating. Our state associations have their own every-other-month call to provide information to their members.

Long before the use of listserves and the like, Len Stein's pathfinding work in Wisconsin, relative to the mission of community care, is a perfect example of the operational leadership needed to embed the innovative mission. While seminal work and scientific breakthroughs are powerful, if they go against established values and traditions, the creative genius of his or her followers will have to exert more direct leadership. In an article titled, "Innovating Against the Current," Len speaks to the operational obstacles that had to be overcome in order to succeed (Stein, 1992). These obstacles include such things as: 1) justifying the training time needed to implement the innovation, 2) mental health aides working in the community without constant supervision, 3) staff using their own cars, 4) staff eating lunch with patients and not counting it as lunch hour, etc. (Stein, 1992).

Len made the point that if the mission (community-based care for people who typically were hospitalized) was contrary and inconsistent with the prevailing mission of the field (hospital-based care), the more creative the operational leadership needed to be in order to get the mission and new organization supported. Fortunately for the mental health field, Len and his colleagues succeeded in getting the first program supported and the idea disseminated.

> In the field of mental health, centralized decision making over the operational process is doomed to failure ....the environment is so complex...[that] leaders at all levels are critical.

In the field of mental health, centralized decision making over the operational process is doomed to failure. As was mentioned in the introductory chapter, the environment is so complex—with various constituencies issuing directives that must be immediately followed, with the courts, the media, advocacy and special interest groups monitoring, reacting to, and encouraging changes in direction—leaders at all levels are critical. When a leader centralizes by mission and decentralizes by operations, obviously it gives more responsibility and authority to line staff and supervisors. However, it also minimizes risk by ensuring that risky organizational initiatives are mission related. In addition, decentralization by operations can exert countervailing forces against those who would overcentralize in an attempt to reduce costs. Overcentralization can reduce organizational output; this happens daily in our current system of care. Utilization review procedures in managed care are an example of this phenomenon (Anthony, 1996a; 1996b). Practitioners who feel a loss of control of their own processes and decisions, and who are constantly questioned by misguided utilization procedures, may end up inadvertently reducing output and ultimately increasing costs.

> When a leader centralizes by mission and decentralizes by operations, obviously it gives more responsibility and authority to line staff and supervisors...It also minimizes risk by ensuring that risky organizational initiatives are mission related.

Leaders at the highest levels of the organization, who overmanage in an attempt to control their operations managers end up, by their example, creating more micromanagers. Rather than create leaders who inspire their staff at the operational level, they create more micromanagers who control their staff through regulations and/or intimidation. Soon the organizational leadership starts to complain that there seems to be an absence of leaders within their organization. This complaint is a diagnosis of the organization's lack of leadership at the highest levels rather than a reflection of the hackneyed phrase that "they don't make leaders like they used to." Larry Kohn, the director of services at the Center for Psychiatric Rehabilitation, knew full well not to micromanage his excellent staff. When Larry left for a different position at the Center, operational leaders such as Dori Hutchinson and Cheryl Gagne easily stepped into leadership roles in the services division (more about Dori and Cheryl in later chapters.)

Leaders who sink too deeply into managing processes for which there are already assigned managers are sealing their future fate. By so doing they are reducing the time they have for reflection and contemplation. Leaders need to distance themselves from the day-to-day battles in order to stimulate their thoughts, as well as the thoughts of others, about refinements in vision, new missions, future mission-related activities based on new information, etc. Some would-be leaders are neither comfortable nor skilled in these requirements of leadership and they retreat to managing others who don't need the attention. Such leaders might as well don a t-shirt that says, "I'm history!"

This is not to say, however, that leaders are oblivious to possible changes that may be made to processes in any area of the organization. The concern over micromanaging does not mean leaders abdicate their role in the operational processes, particularly in times of crisis. In addition, the leader understands that all procedures, no matter how small, reflect on the mission. When the leader notices processes in other folks' operations that seem to be counter to the mission, the leader points them out. Tony Zipple of Thresholds provided some examples.

> The leader understands that all procedures, no matter how small, reflect on the mission. When the leader notices processes in other folks' operations that seem to be counter to the mission, the leader points them out.

You also need to look for ways to lead by changing visible policies and practices. I love to find a policy or procedure that we can make better and which makes our mission more real. For example, when I became CEO, there were pay phones in all programs. We paid a phone company to put them in and collect quarters from our members! We put a plan together and replaced them with phones that were free to members. It cost only a small amount more, but gave members so much access to the world... to friends, family, jobs, etc. And we talked about it as a recovery issue. We also started paying members to be advisors to us. It is not a big check, but it covers their travel costs and a bit more. If we say that we value member perspective, why should they be the only unpaid people in the room? Again, it was a good thing in itself, but it communicated volumes about our mission and values.

Mike Hogan's leadership of the President's Commission (2003) is also relevant to principle 2. Its relevance made sense to us because, in Mike's own words he told us that, as Chairperson of

CENTRALIZE BY MISSION, DECENTRALIZE BY OPERATIONS | 73

the President's Commission, he was trying to "structure and manage a process yielding to a successful outcome." The mission of the President's Commission mission was essentially a given; established through an executive order in which Mike, as chairperson, inherited the marching orders, the timeframes, the members, etc. Yet even within these constraints, there were plenty of opportunities for leadership. Mike's leadership of this commission was guided by a principle that he suggested, and that we incorporated as a task under principle 2. While his leadership experience of the President's Commission did not meet this book's definition of a leader who was leading in a services organization, we thought that the leadership task and experience recounted by Mike was important to be included. Furthermore, Mike had led numerous service organizations himself, and his service leadership efforts are cited throughout this book.

Mike suggested the following principle that we included as a task under principle 2: "Leaders discern what's required and take those actions that are feasible and sufficient for the success of their organization." Surprisingly, perhaps, Mike referenced Robert Heinlein as one of the sources for this suggestion, implying that the right action is taken at the right time because leaders, "understand something so well that is fully absorbed into one's self" (www.whatis.com). Mike affirmed that he needed to discern what would be "sufficient and feasible" for the commission's success based on a full understanding of the functioning of previous commissions.

Early on, Mike set out to understand the implicit or tacit concepts written between the lines of the presidential order establishing the Commission. In order to thoroughly understand the requirements, Mike believed that he needed to understand the origins of the notion of this Commission. Accordingly, he interviewed many policy wonks and read historical source documents. His explorations resulted in a belief that the current president's campaign offer of a mental health presidential commission aligned well with a compassionate, conservative agenda, was politically wise and would be a relatively modest investment of federal attention. In addition, Mike and his colleagues needed to understand the context of commission themselves. Understanding this background led the commission to a strategy that said:

> ...we would try, if possible, to get the federal agencies that are participating excited about this and so engaged that they will take it back later and do good things, whether or not those good things are a direct result of our recommendations. A second strategy was to leave behind a body of work that could be used as a policy and advocacy resource by mental health stakeholders within the Washington, DC, Beltway and that they could use as tools later on down the road.

There would be no major set of regulations, funding or "strong actions and recommendations." But the process would yield resources and a policy direction that could be influential for years to come. Consistent with Mike's collaborative nature, his belief was:

> The commission's process ought to be used as one that was focused on coalition building and consensus deriving rather than technical; to create an environment of collaboration, a feeling that everybody is an empowered participant, and that we are bound together to accomplish a mission of importance.

As a result, public testimony was solicited at every public meeting; every appointed member of the commission was the chair of a subcommittee; consultants were hired to do writing tasks for the subcommittees; meetings were held with individuals of differing ideologies; numerous national conferences were attended and presentations made; a website was created; federal agencies such as the Social Security Administration and the Veterans Administration were engaged, etc.

With Mike's leadership the commission "...discerned what actions would be sufficient and feasible." Out of this process, the vision of recovery emerged as an organizing theme or the "main headline." While not a service organization, the commission report communicated a shared vision that, even before the commission's report, had been adopted by numerous mental health service programs, agencies, and organizations.

As commissioner of mental health in California, during the development, passage, and implementation of California Proposition 63, Steve Mayberg, like Mike Hogan, also had to discern what actions would be sufficient and feasible. Proposition 63 was a California ballot initiative that imposed a 1% tax on personal income of over 1 million dollars a year, with the additional tax revenue used to expand and transform California's public mental health system. The tax was expected to generate over 700 million dollars statewide. It is, at the time of this writing, forecasted to reach close to a billion dollars in revenue.

> Communicating the vision and decentralizing the operation to the grassroots level made people feel as if they owned it.

Demonstrating many of the tasks related to Principle 2, Steve Mayberg was interviewed during Proposition 63's initial implementation. Steve, and others, recognized that to achieve a successful outcome, there were three specific actions or processes that had to be carried out. These required actions included:

- Building a coalition who would speak with one voice about the goal, but who also could trust enough to be brutally honest about the mental health system's strengths and weaknesses;

- Building a system based on the needs of consumers and their families; and

- Understanding why people were not accessing the current system.

We came up with our vision through a lot of work. These were not just words; they were words they came up with by listening to people from multiple trainings, seminars, meetings, and workshops. We figured out what the core values were. People did a great job of staying on message, which took a lot of negotiations before we went public with the message. We spent a lot of time trying to make sure we had everyone on the same page and that everyone agreed that this project was California's mission. We wanted to do it right. We had so much trust and worked very hard together; it was important to us to empower ourselves to be able to get the voters to pass Proposition 63. Communicating the vision and decentralizing the operation to the grassroots level made people feel as if they owned it. They were willing to collect signatures and campaign for it, even if they had never done anything political before, because they had a support system to back them up.

Sometimes leaders need to discern what to stop doing, rather than what to initiate. Kathryn Power spoke about a decision that she had to make when she was commissioner in Rhode Island, prior to becoming the director of CMHS.

> Sometimes leaders need to discern what to stop doing, rather than what to initiate.

In Rhode Island, the consumers basically said we don't think day treatment is working, and we want you to do something about it. I made the decision that I would no longer fund day treatment programs because I visited all the day treatment programs, and I thought that they were a waste of time; consumers said we aren't learning anything. We substituted recovery-oriented supported employment program, and I said that's what I'll pay for.

Kathryn elaborated on the need to discern what mission-related decisions to make when she went on to CMHS, where there were different constraints on what she wanted to do.

Even though we have to do what Congress tells us to do relative to programs, relative to the distribution of funds, relative to granting contracts, we have some responsibility here to make sure that we're doing it in a way that makes sense, and also, how we can figure out collectively ways to help the states and other jurisdictions think about the kind of change that they want in a more transformational way.

Paolo del Vecchio was interviewed when he directed the Office of Consumer Affairs at SAMHSA. (This organization was mentioned previously by Charley Curie and Terry Cline, both of whom led the organization during different parts of Paolo's tenure.) During Paolo's leadership of the Office of Consumer Affairs, there were times when he had to discern what feasible actions should be taken when forces outside his organization's control impeded what he considered "best practice." In the following example, Paolo decided to take a long range view of success.

Practice standards around seclusion and restraint were weakened by the Centers for Medicare and Medicaid Services (CMS) in January, 2007. This is an example of how both my values and SAMHSA values were trumped due to politics. This is another instance where we see governmental actions that support the medical model's approach, which is more focused on coercion than on the human dignity and the worth of people. I mean it's shocking. What do you do in those circumstances? When confronted with policy decisions that do not match your beliefs, you step back and push back. Even when your opinions may not be popular and decisions are made against these beliefs, you continue to articulate these beliefs and principles. Maybe you have to step back and take a longer-term perspective, within yourself, that these important values are right to continue to promote and that this effort may be long term. But you do not give up.

> When confronted with policy decisions that do not match your beliefs, you step back and push back. Even when your opinions may not be popular and decisions are made against these beliefs, you continue to articulate these beliefs and principles.

In contrast to the federal decision on seclusion/restraint (S/R) policy, Charley Curie believed that an earlier S/R reduction initiative implemented in Pennsylvania, when he was the state commissioner, was a "textbook case" with respect to principle 2 (centralizing by mission and decentralizing by operations).

We did not implement formal official policies around S/R for two years after I issued the challenge of reducing S/R in our state hospital system. The challenge was that S/R procedures were not treatment interventions but represented "treatment failures." We had to examine how we were facilitating recovery in the hospitals that are utilizing S/R to a large extent; the answer was we were not. The challenge was that we had a model in one hospital that worked. We needed to figure out how to use the knowledge about that model for systemic change.

I brought the hospital systems' leaders together, including the quality improvement director, the medical directors, and the direct care staff to begin to take a look at what could work in the hospitals to reduce S/R and to identify what elements existed that seemed to contribute to the use of S/R. Over a two-year period several hospitals made great progress without a formal policy on S/R reduction being in place. We were able to pull together what kinds of interventions were working most effectively. This began the process of us pulling together a more formal policy for hospital systems that I signed exactly two years after I issued the challenge. We gave individuals the information; we empowered the employees to be engaged in a problem-solving process and to come up with what would work. We used data to monitor our progress, we initiated healthy competition, rewarded staff for best practices, and created an expectation of transparency regarding what every hospital was accomplishing, including publishing their rates of S/R. The rest is history, and I believe we may be still the largest state hospital system to have eliminated or significantly reduced the use of seclusion and restraint in all of its adult hospitals.

> We gave individuals the information; we empowered the employees to be engaged in a problem-solving process and to come up with what would work.

In summary, the organization, just like the people within it, is empowered when operations are decentralized. We empower the organization by centralizing the mission, and we empower the individual processes of the organization by decentralizing the operations. Leaders of different operations or processes can relate better to one another and work collaboratively when the outcome of each separate process is made explicit and the overall organizational mission is clear.

> The organization, just like the people within it, is empowered when operations are decentralized. We empower the organization by centralizing the mission, and we empower the individual processes of the organization by decentralizing the operations.

When Peter Senge talks about his theory of "learning organizations," he highlights the importance of vision, mission, and empowered employees (Senge, 2006). He strongly believes that key to the development of a viable, flexible organization is voluntary adoption and saturation of an organization's mission and vision throughout the entire system. Senge makes the point that the structures in today's thriving organization are horizontal, not vertical (pyramidal), and this kind of re-deployment of responsibility and power is required.

Structures in today's thriving organization are horizontal, not vertical (pyramidal), and this kind of re-deployment of responsibility and power is required.

3

Leaders create an organizational culture that identifies and tries to live by key values.

- The leader is clear about what values influence organizational decision making.

- The leader uses the organization's values as anchors and guidelines for decisions.

- The leader analyzes operations by how the operations affect the organization's values.

- The leader acknowledges when organizational values conflict.

- The leader's words and behavior are congruent.

- The leader's strategies for achieving the mission are consistent with the organization's values.

- The leader's behavior in the organization reflects the organization's values.

- The leader ensures that the organization's values are the same for everyone in the organization regardless of role.

Leaders create an organizational culture that identifies and tries to live by key values.

Values are the organizational "Velcro" that binds vision to operations.
—*William A. Anthony*

Vision, mission, organizational operations, and values are inextricably woven together. It is no wonder so many leaders mention how their leadership style is guided by principles related to all four of these dimensions. Effective leaders move toward their mission and vision through the practical implementation of organizational values that are reflected in, and congruent with, the daily operational practices observed in their organization.

When Renata Henry was interviewed, she was commissioner for mental health and substance abuse services for the state of Delaware. Under Renata's leadership, the focus of the organization was to create an "integrated, seamless system of care that responds to the consumer wherever he or she enters the door." The values of her organization included creating opportunities in the community, such as accessible and affordable housing opportunities, and crisis and acute care services. Renata's value of "building opportunities in the community" certainly influenced her decision-making. During her very first year, Renata was faced with a crisis that threatened this value of a responsive community system.

> The very first thing that occurred, after I was appointed, was that all hell broke loose in the Delaware State Hospital because we were found out of compliance with what was then HCFA [Health Care Financing Administration] and now CMS [Centers for Medicare

& Medicaid Services] standards in terms of staffing. CMS came in for a surprise survey, and there were threats made to close the hospital. All of this activity was in the local headlines and, in addition, a group of psychiatrists went public about how bad everything was in the hospital. This resulted in a tremendous amount of negative publicity for the hospital and the mental health system. Here I am, six months into this job. How am I going to manage out of this? Because in reality, some of those things that they were saying were true. But I also had developed a vision, and it was focused on the community, with the hospital as an important component, but only one part of the whole system. So I faced the identified problem head-on and said, "yes, all these problems exist, and that's why we've got to get this hospital smaller and really create a strong community system. It is not about the care in the hospital that's bad, it's about the fact that there are too many patients coming into the hospital and no way for them to get back out because there's nothing in the community." In retrospect, it might have been so much easier to just get defensive, but we did not do that. And this became a way to begin to reach the vision of an integrated, seamless system of care that responds to the individual consumer.

During this crisis I sat down with senior staff and thought, okay, so if we could have this ideal system in the community and we could downsize and make the hospital less crowded, what would the system look like? It would mean we would have more housing and group homes, more apartment opportunities; we would have better crisis services in the community; and we also would put acute care in the community. We would stop making the state hospital the focal point of the whole system. If we could build up the community system, we would be able to create more options in the community. So my leadership team and I took this adverse event and turned it around. We saw this set of circumstances as an opportunity and took our vision to help direct us out of this crisis.

Principled leaders resolve operational questions in ways that are consistent with their vision and organization's values. The operations (i.e., processes or activities) in which an organization engages must pass through a "values check." Some leaders call this

"cross-walking organizational policies, procedures, and processes against their values template." (National Executive Training Institutes,
2003). Particularly when there are questions
about whether or how to do a particular
operation or when a mission needs to be
redefined, these are the times when various
alternative ideas need to be weighed against
the organization's values. Leaders need to be
clear about what values are critical to organizational decision making.

> Principled leaders resolve
> operational questions in
> ways that are consistent
> with their vision and
> organization's values.
> The operations...in which
> an organization engages
> must pass through a
> "values check."

Kathy Muscari, from West Virginia, was grounded in certain
values that depicted both her personal beliefs and organizational
culture.

> One of the reasons I became dedicated to the self-help movement
> was my faith in its core values; including respect, choice, responsi-
> bility, knowledge, self-direction, and so forth. As a psychiatric
> rehabilitation counselor and Gestalt therapist, I'm already drawn
> to disciplines where success stems from developing skills and sup-
> ports in the present moment with a focus on honoring others. I
> also had my own life as a personal reminder of how challenging
> experiences can become rewarding opportunities. As a person in
> a leadership role, I encourage team decision-making based on
> organizational values. People who work with me have come to
> know this as an absolute. They've learned the benefits of taking
> time to weigh out agency partnerships, projects, funding, work
> relationships, and such, by examining them through the lens of
> our organizational values. I'm one to say, "As long as it fits our
> mission and values, let's do it!"

Kathy gave an example of how values were used to make a decision about a possible course of action.

> An example of decision-making through values happened when
> our organization had the desire, but not the resources, to conduct
> a national conference on consumer studies. We began to wonder.
> Is this truly a worthy topic? Who else believes in the importance of
> this subject matter? Will they partner? How will we get partici-

pants who want to attend, but have few resources, to the event? Can we secure a comfortable meeting site and expert speakers on a fraying, shoestring budget? These questions were presented to our team who began to apply our values. They said, "Yes, it's a worthwhile topic because it promotes respect and self-direction. Yes, we can name others who will consider joining our efforts because they share our value of promoting knowledge. Yes, we all can choose to chip in so there will be start-up resources, showing responsibility." Not only did we lift our team spirits, we took action. We were able to engage others who became inspired by the evidence of our values at work. As a result, we have had not one, but two such consumer studies conferences and anticipate more. It's simply the right thing to do...because it fits with our mission and values.

Sam Tsemberis provided an example of how one particular organizational value made a seemingly difficult decision obvious. At the time of this writing, Sam was director of Pathways to Housing and a national leader in the field of serving people who are homeless and have a psychiatric disability. Sam's method of housing has been researched periodically, including a randomized clinical trials (Shern et al., 2000; Tsemberis, Gulcur & Nakae, 2004). Choice is a critical value in Sam's organizational values. In the first randomized clinical trial in New York City, Sam was involved in a research study that compared a supported housing program based on psychiatric rehabilitation values to a control condition of "business as usual" for people who were homeless, street dwelling, and diagnosed with severe mental illnesses. A controversy arose as to what to do if a participant chose to continue street dwelling, even though the research outcome was to move into supported housing. Sam said they would continue to help this person no matter where he chose to live, even though this was not an outcome valued by the research funding source. Sam believed that "consumer choice" was a paramount value and must be respected, even if the staff and researchers disagreed with the choice. The people in the program being

> Sam believed that "consumer choice" was a paramount value and must be respected, even if the staff and researchers disagreed with the choice.

researched must have agreed with Sam, as they named the research program "Choices" (Shern et al., 1997).

Steve Mayberg, director of the California Department of Mental Health, reinforced the importance of organizational values by reflecting on how they had to be certain about the words that best captured the organization's values.

> I was really concerned about the references to "system of care." I thought these words were demeaning and not as empowering as words should be. I wanted to describe what we were doing and did not want it to sound like traditional community treatment, so we did not want to call it system of care. So we called it "community services and supports" because these were the values that we wanted to offer.

Steve and his colleagues also changed the name of mental health services to "full service partnerships" to encourage and reflect the priority value that consumers and families are partners in the services.

In the field of mental health, the leaders who have previously been trained as clinicians and/or researchers sometimes let their textbook training unduly influence their capacity to define an organization's values. Principles, such as clinical objectivity and scientific rigor, have sometimes overwhelmed the field's search for other values. The mental health field's historical quest for objectivity, distance, avoidance of risks, and professional boundaries, etc., can confuse the mental health leaders' understanding of the importance of specifying values that are recovery-oriented and person-centered. The traditional emphasis in mental health, if one were trained clinically or experimentally, often was to try to eliminate the impact of one's own personal values in the name of objectivity and rigor. Traditionally, to be guided by one's values was to unduly influence the clinical relationship or the empirical process.

> The mental health field's historical quest for objectivity, distance, avoidance of risks, and professional boundaries, etc., can confuse the mental health leaders' understanding of the importance of specifying values that are recovery oriented and person centered.

Dori Hutchinson was trained as both a clinician and a researcher. When Dori was interviewed, she was director of services at the Boston University Center for Psychiatric Rehabilitation. As described in a previous chapter, the educational and rehabilitation services provided to people with severe mental illnesses were offered on the Boston University campus. Her clinical and research training did not prevent her from using recovery principles as her "values anchor" and guidelines for decision making.

I believe the most challenging aspect of my job as a director of services is keeping the recovery values alive in the day-to-day life and practices of our services. Regardless of how committed my staff is to the values of choice, personhood, self-determination, etc., when we are confronted with a difficult issue or a challenging person, there is this incredible regression to nonrecovery-based behavior and emotions. I believe my utmost responsibility is to be the "keeper of the values" in these day-to-day conflicts. A great example of this is in our computer classes. We teach computer skills on computers that have access to the Internet. Almost as soon as we connected to the Internet, people began to surf the pornographic sites during open computer time. Immediately the staff was outraged and wanted to install barriers to these sites that would prevent anyone from looking at any "inappropriate content." Staff were upset, angry, and worried.

> Regardless of how committed my staff is to the values of choice, personhood, self-determination...when we are confronted with a difficult issue or a challenging person, there is this incredible regression to nonrecovery-based behavior and emotions. I believe my utmost responsibility is to be the "keeper of the values" in these day-to-day conflicts.

Of course we want our services environment to be safe for everyone, and there are many people who have histories of violence and trauma that may be triggered by seeing pornographic images. But we serve adults, and the fact is that for adults, looking at adult pornographic material is not against the law. We looked into how the University deals with the issue, and they take the stance that such viewing should not be done in classrooms or on public university computers, but was up to the learner in the privacy of the students' homes.

In the services division, we state that we value the personhood of each adult with serious mental illness that comes to us for service. I felt that rather than installing software on the computers that would prevent access, we should honor the capacity for our service recipients to act like adults and take responsibility for their behavior. I suggested that we have a policy that is consistent with how the university treats everyone with respect to public use of computers. Accordingly, we asked our service recipients to refrain from viewing sexual or violent websites as it lessens the safe and nurturing environment of the services programs. If students were unable to refrain from viewing these sites, we would restrict their access to the computers. I believed this approach would treat our service recipients like all the other adults in the university community, rather than children, or worse, criminals. Initially, I was met with great resistance and resentment from the staff that thought I was taking a clinically inappropriate stance. The intensity of people's feelings towards my values-based decision was and is difficult at times to endure. It can be a very lonely experience for me at times. I felt very discouraged by these glimpses of people's prejudices. But time has proven this decision about internet access to be consistent with our values and our mission. We do have a couple of service recipients who have difficulty resisting the temptation to surf these types of sites (as many adults without psychiatric illnesses do, I might add), so we do not allow them to use the Internet while they are in our public computer room.

We accomplish the operationalization of personhood and personal responsibility as well as the creation of a nurturing, respectful environment by treating people with serious mental illnesses as the adults they are. Sometimes it requires modeling personal responsibility or teaching the skills and supports so folks can operationalize the value in their own lives. To me as the "leader," that is the easy part. The challenge is supporting my staff to trust that operationalizing the value of personhood is the right thing to do and the only way to do it. This takes a lot of time and constantly responding to the negative feelings staff may have towards me because I stand guard over the value, while at the same time not wavering from my commitment to the value.

> We accomplish the operationalization of personhood and personal responsibility as well as the creation of a nurturing, respectful environment by treating people with serious mental illnesses as the adults they are.

Unlike the example provided by Dori, historically when people trained as clinicians and/or scientists became leaders of mental health organizations, they often brought their trained reluctance to identity and integrate values into the organization itself. In such instances, the culture of the organization will be valueless without the leaders strong stand on what values matter most to the organization. The absence of a strong statement about values became, in fact, the major organizational value. As a result, the operations were not typically evaluated by how they affected the consensually defined values of the organization.

In contrast, exemplary leaders of mental health in this current era are very certain that organizational values need to be specified. There were no apologies from the principled leaders interviewed for being part of an organizational culture that specifies quite clearly certain key values. Their clinical and/or research training did not get in the way of their leadership style with respect to the need to have an organizational culture steeped in values. Remember how Kim Ingram of Thomasville, Alabama, quashed her state hospital's "levels program" because it was not consistent with the organizational vision? The "levels program's" demise was made even easier because it was incompatible with a major organizational value of self-determination.

> We frequently request feedback from program participants during meetings in which we review our values and ask them to come up with examples of how we've stayed true or fallen short of the values.

Cheryl Gagne, a colleague of Dori Hutchinson, was interviewed when she was associate director of services at the Boston University Center for Psychiatric Rehabilitation. Cheryl had been a consumer of services in both the mental health and substance abuse system, and subsequently had received her doctorate in psychiatric rehabilitation. She shared Dori's emphasis on analyzing the consistency between the organization's activities and its expressed values.

The values that drive our program are articulated and posted. We make these explicit so that program participants can assist us in staying true to our values. We frequently request feedback from program participants during meetings in which we review our values and ask them to come up with examples of how we've stayed true or fallen short of the values. In staff meetings, we also review our values and have conducted "stop-start-continue" exercises to review program policies, procedures, and activities to assure adherence to our values.

Cheryl picked up again with how the leadership tried to live by the organization's values, and encouraged everyone in the organization to do likewise.

We also try to live these values in our relationships with coworkers. We treat each other with respect, support the growth potential in each other, and recognize individual strengths and needs. We support each other in living up to these values and give feedback to each other regarding how well we are living up to our values. We recognize that living our values requires a daily commitment and effort. When things get difficult, many of the younger, less experienced staff revert into behavior that is not consistent with our values. They want to develop policies to control and regulate the behavior of program participants rather than work with the program participant in a relationship, teaching skills and offering support, to help the individual meet the demands of the environment. It requires strong and constant leadership to assist staff with these challenges.

> We...try to live these values in our relationships with coworkers. We treat each other with respect, support the growth potential in each other, and recognize individual strengths and needs.

Most recently, with the advent of managed care approaches, the value of cost containment has become preeminent in some organizations. While cost containment, per se, does not seem to be an overriding value of many of the current leaders interviewed, leaders who are comfortable in articulating their values seem to see cost containment as only one of many important values.

Leaders in managed care must understand that no organization of substance has survived with cost containment as its only value. Recovery-oriented services for people

> Leaders in managed care must understand that no organization of substance has survived with cost containment as its only value.

with severe mental conditions also are guided by values, such as consumer growth, empowerment, and self-determination. The importance of values, other than cost containment, is not to say however that cost containment, profit seeking, or reducing government expenditures and taxes are "dirty words." In this sense, cost containment is a neutral term. It's how you accomplish containing costs that's critical. Did the organization add something of value to the mission other than profit or tax relief?

> It's how you accomplish containing costs that's critical. Did the organization add something of value to the mission other than profit or tax relief?

For example, if you sell someone a car for fifty percent less, but the car does not work, the money you save the customer is irrelevant. If you cut mental health costs by managed care initiatives, but the managed care services don't help get consumers from point A to point B, then you are in fact not a principled leader. The promise to provide effective services does not dissipate because one has simply cut costs. The bottom line is to make a profit or minimize taxes through acts of integrity. The public and private mental health sectors still have much to learn about cost-effective business practices. Important key values need to guide services, and business practices need to support a workforce to provide these services. Too often we see a traditional service system where long-standing historic practices, services, and contracts are continued despite the lack of evidence or outcomes associated with these services.

Profits cannot be placed above the value that, first and foremost, a quality service that provides expected outcomes needs to be delivered. The American car manufacturers learned this fact from the Japanese automakers, that a single-minded focus on profit can overwhelm more critical values that lead to the deterioration of the product or service.

The first full privatization of a public state mental health facility provides some lessons learned regarding the importance of values other than simple corporate profit. As narrated by KH:

> The privatization of the hospital known as South Florida State Hospital (SFSH) in Pembroke Pines, Florida, had a rocky start. After years of re-occurring problems in clinical care, risk management

issues, budgetary shortfalls, sentinel events, administrative turnover, aging facilities, and an inability to even apply for JCAHO accreditation, the Florida Legislature ordered the Florida Department of Health and Human Services to privatize this beleaguered facility. This decision engendered much negative media attention, protests by unionized staff members, and understandable reluctance by the state mental health agency. The privatization proposal was sent out in 1997 and was awarded to an organization then known as the Wackenhut Corporation (now GEO Care, Inc.).

On October 31, 1998, Wackenhut (now GEO Care, Inc.) took over SFHS. This "takeover" was viewed with some apprehension by both the state employees and some of the leadership staff who had been hired and were former public mental health employees. But within a few months Wackenhut demonstrated their corporate values that included providing effective, efficient, and outcome-based services that were designed to meet the difficult outcomes called for in their contract with the state of Florida. Not only did SFSH retain as many state employees as were willing to stay, but also did this work with 200 fewer FTEs [due to state bumping processes and normal attrition] than when the state had managed the hospital.

All of the benchmarks (outcomes) for the hospital's operation that were set by Florida's state mental health authority were met and exceeded. These outcomes included building a new, state-of-the-art hospital on the grounds with no funding from the state; acquiring JCAHO accreditation within one year (or face a $1,000,000 fine); accelerating discharges and admissions in a hospital that had been "gridlocked for years where people who needed services often waited in community programs for up to one year"; regaining the trust of the community; reducing elopements and recidivism according to set benchmarks; reducing injuries to persons served and staff; and providing "active treatment" based on the Boston University approach to psychiatric rehabilitation.

In addition to the expectations noted above, the hospital staff were able to almost eliminate seclusion and restraint use.

What is most important in the lessons learned by those of us who had the opportunity to participate in this successful and eye-opening project was that when a state decides to privatize a facility, clear outcomes must be documented, and consequences for a contractor's failure to produce must be defined. Equally important was the matching of public sector values that stayed true to the needs of the people served, private sector business practices that allowed progress in a much more rapid manner than could ever have been seen in the public sector, and an expected level of accountability rarely reached in the public sector. Two of many examples include: 1) the ability to purchase 20 bicycles in 3 days for the newly created consumer "exercise club" and 2) the ability to hire peer advocates into vacant nursing positions within days. Also important was the new executive management group's ability to change policy and procedures quickly and to reward and recognize staff who were performing beyond expectations, without a lot of bureaucratic red tape. This project was and is a resounding success and has been replicated in other facilities since. And notably, the first management group all moved on to new projects by 2003, and the successes seen in ASH/SFSH in Pembroke Pines, Florida, remain a tribute to sustainability and the public and corporate values that meshed and "took" in an outcome-oriented manner.

Martha Long was interviewed when she was director of the Village, a capitated program that she directed from the very beginning of its existence. At the time of the interview, the Village of Long Beach, California, was one of two comprehensive Integrated Services Agencies created by the California legislature to serve people with severe mental illnesses through a capitated fiscal design. However, it was so much more than a program designed to contain costs through capitation. One of us (WA) met with Martha and her staff at the Village over dinner, attended a team meeting and a student training seminar, participated in an organizational strategic planning meeting, and observed staff and clients interact. (Anthony, 1993a).

The mission statement of the Village at that time was, "to encourage the empowerment of adults with psychiatric disabilities to successfully live, socialize, learn, and work in the community." The Village's values were consistent with the mission, and staff at all levels were cognizant of the agency's key values, such as consumer choice, consumer work opportunities, and member driven. In order to create an organizational culture, staff were selected or retained based in part on their agreement with agency values. According to Martha, trying to get an organization to live by key values also helped some professionals leave the organization when they saw that their helping strategies did not mesh with the organization's underlying values. For example, Martha recounted how a psychiatrist who eventually left the organization was worried about transference issues if people were treated as people by staff! Martha often used stories to reinforce the key values of the organization. She often used examples of Village members' improvement in the Village culture that were not able to progress in other settings; she told repeatedly the stories of the culture's positive influence. In particular, Martha made sure stories of the "stars" were told, so people would realize that, "if she could do it, so could I."

Martha believed that it was always important to take the time to understand the meaning of different organizational values. The value of "member-driven services" was viewed incorrectly by some to mean that staff did not have input into member decision making. But to Martha, the value "member driven" meant that choice was taken seriously. To illustrate how seriously choice was taken, Martha gave an example of a staff member who complained, "What am I going to do? So and so wants to run for President, that's the plan he wants to work on?" To illustrate the point of how important it is to start from the members' frame of reference, Martha remarked, "Well, find out what primary he is filing in and how many signatures he needs, and you go from there."

> Organizational values provide the anchor points and guidelines for decisions throughout the organization.

Organizational values provide the anchor points and guidelines for decisions throughout the organization. No matter what a person's role in the organization is, leaders assure that values mean the same for everyone. The values are translated into normative behavior that drives the entire organization. The organization's values show everyone what is important to the organization. Values define the corridors in which an organization functions. Values should be clear, evoke passion, and have consensus throughout the organization.

> Values should be clear, evoke passion, and have consensus throughout the organization.

Judi Chamberlin was interviewed some years after she had established and had been the director of the Ruby Rogers Advocacy and Drop-In Center in Massachusetts. Judi stressed the importance of the organization's values being the same for everyone in the organization regardless of role.

From previous experiences in services operated by consumers/survivors of mental health services, I had a good idea of what a consumer-operated service would look like. I had worked with a number of consumer-run programs and had written about them in my book, *On Our Own: Patient-Controlled Alternatives to the Mental Health System* (1978). Few of the people involved with me in establishing the Ruby Rogers Center had this kind of experience; they were used to top-down, professionally-run services, and although they were enthusiastic about the idea of a consumer-run service, many did not have a good idea of how such a service would operate. It was, therefore, very important that I constantly transmit the values of consumer-operated programs, and that I ensured that leadership was shared and decisions were collectively made, even when members would say things like, "it's too difficult, you do it." It was, therefore, very gratifying the first time the membership voted to do something different from what I wanted to do!

Also in Massachusetts, in a very different role and years later, Elizabeth Childs, commissioner of mental health, had this to say about the importance of clearly defined organizational values.

> The only way to be successful in a leadership role is to not only have the formal authority provided by your position title and the state statutes that govern this role, but also to use your moral authority.

I feel that the only way to be successful in a leadership role is to not only have the formal authority provided by your position title and the state statutes that govern this role, but also to use your moral authority. Effective moral authority is not possible without identifying absolutely clear, razor sharp, values that help describe what the leader really stands for. And they can't be something you just wear or adopt; they have to be something that's intrinsic to how you think and how you feel about people. In mental health, I would say that important values in mental health today are putting the person first, listening to a person carefully regarding their needs and hopes, and having the courage to take on advocacy roles that often are not very popular.

Elizabeth continued on as to how the leaders' actions must be congruent with their expressed values.

I think effective leadership is about courage, listening, and sometimes, humility about what we know and what we don't know. Effective leadership requires a genuine belief in people. That people get better and do recover. You have to believe it in your bones that what you are doing has value to people, and their families, and the community in general. If you don't have that, I don't think it's possible to have moral authority. I don't think moral authority is one of those things that you have to be upfront about; you don't have to be screaming about it at the top of your lungs. You don't have to state that you have moral authority; you have to demonstrate your moral authority. If there's anything we know in mental health, it's that words are cheap. It's

> You don't have to state that you have moral authority; you have to demonstrate your moral authority.

really my actions that demonstrate whether or not I will make decisions that are difficult but that are based on my values. I think you want your team to "get this" very clearly, very quickly, and understand that they may test you. As a leader, I get presented with problems and sometimes a lot of pressure to do things the "old way." People asked me to make decisions based on the content of the single questions they posed, but I think that leadership decisions are even more important in terms what they tell the people that report to you, about what you believe.

I'll give an example. We were providing services to a young man with a complicated co-occurring condition, who lived outside of Boston in a suburban area. He had been moved into a house in his hometown right down the street from his family. And it became a huge political show. Even though he had graduated from the high school in that town and his family lived there, the town did not want him in this specialized housing program that we had for young adults with mental illnesses. We were getting incredible pressure from the town, from state officials, from the governor's office, from the press, you name it. Every constituency group was giving us a lot of pressure. I remember it was early on, and I was very new. I remember sitting around the table and saying to my senior team, "I don't care what all of these other people are telling me, I want to know what's in the best interest of this young man?" Someone said to me later that they couldn't believe that I said that because here was a man who had committed a felony and who had a serious mental illness, and I was more concerned what was in his best interest than everybody else's best interest. And we did figure out what was in his best interest and the outcome was that it actually was not in his best interest to stay in the house because he couldn't even walk out the door without being targeted. We got him into a program that I think was probably more effective for him and got him the services he really needed. I made clear that our decisions were to be made from what he needed, and we would deal with all the other constituencies. I went to town meetings; we had legislative meetings, every kind of meeting with all the stakeholders to explain our position. I think when you hold out, when your values are clear; it's much easier to deal with the forces that come at you to try to pull you off your value-based stance. I think there are a lot of variables that come into play and try to move you away from your values; it does take a lot of courage to stay true to your values.

> There are a lot of variables that come into play and try to move you away from your values; it does take a lot of courage to stay true to your values.

Elizabeth gave yet another example of how values can serve as anchors and guidelines for decision making.

Another example, regarding the need for effective leaders to have courage and be clear on their values, would be the Massachusetts' statewide seclusion and restraint reduction initiative. My office received a lot of pressure from some of our medical associations, that hold a lot of authority in Massachusetts, when we sent out our new regulations for their review. I remember I was in a meeting with groups of physicians who were saying "How can you expect us to be at the bedside in an hour when somebody's in restraints? It's going to ruin our lives; we aren't set up to do that." But I firmly believed, and still do, that the use of seclusion or restraint is a medical emergency and involves a real person in a potentially life and death situation. No physician would question the need to be to be at the bedside when somebody is having a cardiac event or some other physical health emergency, and this was no different. And I think it was the use of this kind of metaphor and my getting clear about what we were talking about that helped get through these objections and get these new regulations promulgated.

Elizabeth acknowledged how values-based decision making can lead to conflict.

I had to clarify to the physicians that this expectation was much more than being interrupted at dinner. That we were talking, perhaps, about an extra trip back to the hospital, but for a reason that was not really negotiable. We were talking about somebody who is in the most serious mental health crisis we could imagine, besides suicide or an adverse and serious medication reaction. A procedure that usually involves a struggle and a takedown always raises the specter of sudden unexpected death resulting from a combination of catecholamine release, unknown cardiac anomalies, medications, compromised respiratory issues, etc. It's hard to explain, sometimes, why a seclusion or restraint event, often involving a violent "takedown" is so important because it seems so clear-cut when you step back from it, at least to me. But when you're in the throes of being confronted with incredible pressure from your own colleagues, you have to balance these conflicts because you recognize your need to have these same colleagues work with you, to march forward with your goals, so to speak; to be leaders too. You can't alienate everybody or you can't get anything done. There is a tendency to settle for less, sometimes, less than you wanted, and leaders must be judicious in compromising

> There are times to compromise, but only when this compromise does not sell out your priority values.

their values. I think there are times to compromise, but only when this compromise does not sell out your priority values. In the case of the Massachusetts' seclusion and restraint regulations, we compromised very little as it would not have been consistent with our organizational values that were backed by current best practices.

As Elizabeth Childs' example illustrated, values can at times cause conflict within an organization. The leaders of the organization understand that sometimes decisions need to be made that satisfy one organizational value but not another. Leaders who have articulated their values have an easier time of acting contrary to one particular value when they know their actions complement other key values. Richard Surles, as the commissioner of the New York State Office of Mental Health, valued community-based care.

> Leaders who have articulated their values have an easier time of acting contrary to one particular value when they know their actions complement other key values.

Yet he believed that there were times when this value could be subjugated for another, as when he agreed to keep state hospitals open in order to win other battles. Richard felt that a leader needed to be an opportunist who had to take advantage of whatever mission and value-related opportunities came along. He stated that he would "refuse to throw myself on the values sword" when he was trying to get the system to make massive change. In other words, he would not permit adherence to one particular value stop system progress in other areas. In this regard, he tried to run many different strategies that were consistent with organizational values, but he did not wish to be identified with only one strategy. If an opportunity occurred then he would run with that strategy. For example, he implemented a strategy to improve the mental health care of New York State veterans by taking advantage of a CBS "60 Minutes" story on a veteran. Richard used that "60 Minutes" program as a springboard to meet with the federal Veterans Administration (VA) in Washington, DC. The federal VA and the New York State Office of Mental Health developed a cooperative agreement, whereas the VA would provide mental health and physical health care for veterans, while

New York State would provide case management and residential services.

Values can conflict at all levels of the organization's processes. Clinical policies, procedures, and processes must constantly attempt to be consistent with the value base of the organization, as was the case with clinical team meetings at the Village in California. In one example of the difficulty of keeping the Village's clinical process and the organizational values on the same page, one of us (WA) saw a team struggle with a member's choice not to go to work on that particular day for what the staff considered to be a very poor reason. The values conflict for staff was to show respect for the member's choice versus the importance of the member developing a worker identity. In this instance, staff decided to send a person to the member's home to encourage him to come to work that day. This decision was made after discussing the values that guide and anchor the agency's activities. The organization's operations, be they clinical or managerial, must be seen as consistent. A clinical process that values consumer self-determination cannot easily co-exist with a management process that values control and compliance, also known as "obedience."

> A clinical process that values consumer self-determination cannot easily co-exist with a management process that values control and compliance.

Carlos Brandenburg from Nevada mentioned the resistance that had to be overcome as he led his organization to value that:

> The consumer needed to be the principle party in this relationship, that we all worked for the consumer. That if the consumer was satisfied, then we would be satisfied. Our division had been characterized in the traditional way; the consumer comes in, the consumer is treated as a consumer, and treatment is dictated to them. I said, "No, I want the consumer to be an active participant. We work for the consumer; we are responsive to the consumer." Consumers needed to participate in their decisions, and that value expected that they needed to be an active member of the whole treatment process.

Carlos remembered that it was a highly placed staff member who argued the most against these non-traditional values.

One senior leader really did not understand the need to have the consumer involved. He was from the old school basically—patients come in, patients are seen, patients are treated, and patients go on their way. And he didn't quite understand the need for us to have consumers participate in their treatment plan. So it took a long time, but that's where I think the mission and vision basically made it very, very clear what my expectations were of the organization. At that time, it was almost like putting a rudder back on the ship.

For principled leaders like Carlos, it was often the case that the values implicit in the vision of recovery, and the magnitude of system change that needed to occur to align the organization with these recovery-based values, created conflict with the organizational values of a system that had been built on non-recovery based values. As expressed by Kathryn Power when she was the head of CMHS:

One of the big issues with values is: what do you do when you come into an organization and the values of system transformation toward recovery just conflict with the old values? I've been in organizations (and here I don't mean CMHS) that didn't even know how to spell the word recovery. As a leader, you have to really take on a different kind of role. I think there are a number of ways in which leadership gets expressed; sometimes you have to express it in a way that just tells people what you want. Their minds and hearts will follow because they have to follow you because you pay them, or you're their leader. This is very authoritarian and very hierarchical, but sometimes that's what you have to do. You have to go into organizations that do not have a clue sometimes about what the values are or what the values should be, and say, "these are our values. If you do not embrace them or follow them or make them your own and therefore behave in ways that I can see that you've made them your own, you don't need to be in this organization anymore." So I've done it that way too.

> There are a number of ways in which leadership gets expressed; sometimes you have to express it in a way that just tells people what you want.

When David Shern was interviewed he had just been appointed CEO of Mental Health America. (Read more about David's previous stellar work in New York State as recounted by Richard Surles in chapter 8.) In his interview, however, David revisited his leadership experience as the dean of the Florida Mental Health Institute (FMHI) at the University of South Florida. In the role of dean, David also was responsible for the service programs that had been run by FMHI, in the past. Like Kim Ingram's thoughts on Thomasville's levels program, David thought the FMHI services were in conflict with the organization's mission and values.

> We had one residential treatment facility that we continued to run on-site and it was a million dollar operation annually. It was a token economy program for adults. From my perspective, it wasn't state of the art at all. I did not think it was best practice. It was not generative at all of current research, although the staff was recording all of these behaviors. They had people counting every behavior you could imagine. There were no grants being supported as a result of it. So we went through a process of exploring what was going on; we brought in some external consultants, which is also another good strategy, to have people come in and provide you with some advice. As a result, we decided to close that program down, which as you might imagine, caused some ripples. Our direction and our values were not about running our own programs; we were about working with people who were actually running programs in the real world and trying to assist them through the generation of knowledge and through information support. The residential program's closing seemed to set a good concrete example in that regard.

It is up to organizational leadership to make values tangible, not only through their work, but also through their behaviors. Leaders must live by the same rules as their staff. How leaders spend their time, what questions they ask, in what projects they show interest, their reactions to critical incidences, all reflect on that organization's values. Besides the consistency that must exist between the leader's words and actions, the values must be consistent between various members of the organization. That is, the organizational leadership strives to have the values deeply shared by all the people in the organization.

Joe Swinford was interviewed when he was in charge of the Office of Consumer Affairs in Tennessee and the president of the National Association of Consumer/State Mental Health Administrators (NACSMHA). As a result, he was in a great position to be aware of the difficulties in how values conflict, and how, with respect to values, such as self-determination and choice, leadership may "talk the talk, but not walk the walk." Joe commented:

> How leaders spend their time, what questions they ask, in what projects they show interest, their reactions to critical incidences, all reflect on that organization's values.

I think the principle regarding the importance of organizational leadership's implementation of organizational values is the most challenging principle in our current mental health culture. When you start talking about values, such as sharing personal experiences, of including and promoting people with a mental illness, and of allowing people to take risks and learn consequences; this is where I see the breakdown. And there still remains that strong and more overriding value of protecting the community and protecting that vulnerable person that conflicts with the value of allowing people to take risks, to try to step back and accept challenges on their own, and to deal with that fear of failure. We, the system, are risk aversive. I certainly see this conflict a lot with some of the struggles between NAMI and our national consumer association.

Joe dealt with this values conflict by acknowledging when values were in conflict, first listening to people who espoused values other than his, and then choosing the right time to promote consumer friendly values.

I have a value of hearing people out, even if the first few words out of their mouths make me want to jump across the table. I really try to live a value of suspending judgment and listening uncritically to what's coming across; I think that has helped to me to diffuse conflicts and to facilitate a lot of discussions where I can be genuinely accepted by providers and by our consumers. This is a really big challenge particularly for state directors of the Office of Consumer Affairs. I think that if you really want to be an effective consumer administrator, you've got to be able to listen to what everyone has to say without critically judging, even when the providers only focus on the business impact and the financial impact of making some of these changes and adjustments; we need to understand what that is about and why it is important and value that side. I mean those are real concerns. At the same time, I must look for ways to interject those values of recovery and consumer empowerment in ways that they will not be threatening to them.

Scott Graham had an interesting way to make sure everyone in the organization knew what the critical values of the organization were. When Scott was interviewed, he was executive director of Revisions in Maryland, a psychosocial rehabilitation program. Prior to that position he had directed another psychosocial rehabilitation program, Boley Manor in Florida (Connors, Graham & Pulso, 1987; Graham, 1982). Scott gave every staff person a wallet sized, laminated card with the mission and key values printed on it. Scott saw this as yet another way to reinforce the critical importance of the mission and values, and to encourage staff to remember the specific values and mission that guided their practice.

Sharing the same values throughout the organization does not mean individuals do not have their own unique values. While certain values express the shared values of the organization, others are individually expressed. For example, a person's belief in certain religious values may be more apt to be seen as shared organizational values when they are working for an organization that is run by a church. Otherwise those religious values may not be the shared values of that organization—just the unique values of the individual. As was pointed out previously, Cindy Barker was very committed to her mission of the mobile drop-in center and the necessity for a "normal" looking van to transport the people. Yet Cindy also made sure that people's individual values, including her own (e.g., spiritual values), were not imposed

> Sharing the same values throughout the organization does not mean individuals do not have their own unique values.

on anyone by the organization. Cindy believed that the organizational values, such as community integration and self advocacy were very clear, and it was only these organizational values that influenced organizational decision making.

The leader must talk continuously about the organization's key values. The stories, metaphors, anecdotes, and celebrations that reflect the organization's clinical culture must fit with the expressed values of the organization. Similar to the way the leader must constantly reinforce the organization's vision, the leader must act in a like-minded way with respect to the organization's critical values. Estelle Douglas was director of psychiatric rehabilitation at Hillside Hospital in New York when she was interviewed. Estelle was constantly reminding the entire hospital organization about the importance of the value of choice for the people who were hospitalized. Estelle and her team had to "stick to our guns" no matter the hostility that arose against what we were trying to do. She said they had to be vigilant about maintaining our program's values. Unfortunately, in contrast to what Estelle was trying to do, she stated that patients often were seen by others as "stupid or unmotivated" when it came to pursuing goals. Estelle remarked:

> The leader must talk continuously about the organization's key values. The stories, metaphors, anecdotes, and celebrations that reflect the organization's clinical culture must fit with the expressed values of the organization.

> Every time we had a staff meeting, our job was to educate the doctors and administrators that rehabilitation was possible. The main argument that we would get from the doctors was that if you ask "mental patients" what they want to do, they all want to be rock stars. I've been doing psych rehab for twenty years and not one wanted to be a rock star. Some did want to be psychoanalysts, however.

Values that are organizationally specific and shared also can help staff to reframe what they see as a problem. When the organization runs a value check on a problem, the problem may redefine itself and no longer be a problem. Two different organizations that use the same value word as part of each organization's values may find that they define the value word operationally in very different

terms—based on their organizational structure. This differential definition can occur
even within the same organization.

There are teachable moments that leaders use to reinforce the organization's values.
Leaders often reframe failures as a learning
experience. They may use this time to reflect on their values and
to discuss what their most important values really are. The times
when values conflict is another good time for a discussion about
values. The tension created by a value conflict can be used to passionately discuss the importance and ranking of particular organizational values. Remember how Sam Tsemberis, the director of the
Pathways to Housing organization, used the conflict between the
value of "choice" versus the value of "positive outcome" to reinforce the value of choice as the primary value, thus overriding the
researchers' critical value of achieving the positive outcomes as
defined by the researchers. This was the same conundrum faced by
Atlantic Shores (now GEO Care, Inc.)/South Florida State Hospital's
Bob Quam when resolving the conflict between the "safety
mantra" inherent in the hospital's traditional rules versus the facts
that these rules were causing constant conflict that sometimes led
to aggression and the use of seclusion or restraint. The reduction
of unnecessary institutional rules, such as restrictive visiting,
phone access hours, and wake-up and bed times were changed to
be more congruent with the predominant
organizational value that supported individual needs and choices, in concert with this
hospital's focus on recovery principles.

The various operational processes of the
organization may differ with respect to how
well these unique organizational processes
are guided by the organizational values.
When a particular process operates incompatibly with the organization's values, the leader may have to step in and provide direction. For example, Charley Curie believed the values of consistency and fairness needed to be re-emphasized in one part of the
SAMSHA culture, i.e., the process of screening federal grant applications. Charley noted:

> When the organization runs a value check on a problem, the problem may redefine itself and no longer be a problem.

> The tension created by a value conflict can be used to passionately discuss the importance and ranking of particular organizational values.

An example I can talk about is what I call the "screen out" grant fiasco. When I got to SAMHSA there was a situation that arose and had been going on for years, not only at SAMHSA but other federal agencies, where you have "screen out" criteria for people who apply for grants. The screen out criteria could include: "margins have to be so wide, and it can't be off by an ⅛th inch on that side of the paper, and your font can't be too big." The reason that these had been developed was to eliminate applicants from trying to squeeze in three times the words so they would have a better advantage over others in their application process. I had given guidance to my staff that I didn't want us to be "weenie-headed bureaucrats," or lose out on some of the best ideas out there. I also have regards for the fact you want to keep a level of reliability, consistency, and balance.

Charley offered more information about this ongoing saga.

Following the guidance I thought I had provided, I received complaints by some state mental health commissioners about how they were screened out based on being off an ⅛th inch on their margins. Then I got a letter from a senator complaining about how grantees were handled. This was six months after I had issued the guidance on how we want to touch people we work with, how I want us to be viewed, and yet the whole thing was already starting to fall apart. I came back and asked folks about my message and what they had heard. They said "my" new directions were for 2004 and that they were in the middle of 2003. I realized that I had not been clear and said that this new way of managing grants could start now because it is hurting us now. Some staff were finding it easier to screen out because it decreased the number of grant applications they had to review. This concerned me because the field was already suspicious that this was happening anyway. So we intervened and managed it from my office to really examine the consistency through out SAMHSA. We now have people submit the grant application online; it is much easier to manage now, to count words and to focus on the content, not the margins.

Kim Ingram from Thomasville, Alabama gave an example of how her leadership team used the organization's stated values to help guide them through a difficult clinical decision—a decision with seemingly no "right" answer. Kim stated that the Thomasville leadership team was guided by three key values, for both residents and staff. These values were choice, empowerment, and feeling successful and satisfied. Choice was a very difficult value to implement for an inpatient facility, but nevertheless it did anchor their decision making. Getting all staff to believe that people are capable of making choices and decisions for themselves remained problematic. As an illustration of this difficulty, Kim told the story of a voluntary patient who wanted to leave on foot on a Sunday to hitchhike to Mobile and then on to Georgia. Consistent with the value of self-determination and choice, the patient was not prevented from leaving, but they talked to him about coming back if he had difficulty with the trip. They also wanted him to wait until Monday when they could be more helpful in arranging transportation, but he was determined to leave. He left and returned very quickly. Kim stated he is now working even harder on his rehabilitation plans and his eventual recovery. He said to Kim, "I made a bad choice."

There are times when the leader analyzes the organization's values and the organization is found wanting. Tom Lane from Florida implemented a major project within his division that he knew would challenge some long held beliefs and values that were counterproductive to the vision of recovery.

> The Career Development Internship Program, or the CDI project as it came to be known, involved hiring people receiving services as temporary part-time employees for a period of up to six months. We developed a job description, established a fair wage of eight dollars an hour, and put the word out to staff. The project was very controversial, but it quickly grew, and continues today. To date, approximately 40 individuals have graduated from the Career Development Internship Program. Some have returned to school and are attending the local community college, some have become permanent employees, and some have gone on to establish their own businesses.

Tom's CDI project has had a major impact on the people who became staff for this project.

> They saw themselves not as clients or patients—they were employees. They had a badge and got a paycheck every other Friday. Many of them had been in services for years. When their peers saw them working, saw them begin to talk about going to a movie on the weekend, or saw them buy a used car, it changed the way they thought about themselves. Most amazing and most rewarding, being a career development intern brought hope for a better life, brought hope that things are getting better, and gave the people working as CDIs an eagerness to share that message of hope with their peers. The Career Development Internship Program was a catalyst for transforming the culture not only in the agency, but in the entire district.

Tom recounted an example of how difficult the implementation of the CDI project was for staff that did not share the values underlying the vision of recovery.

> I remember one particularly eye-opening experience, the first time paychecks for the first group of CDIs were cut. One person was so concerned the CDI paychecks were mixed in with everyone else's. "What if they see my address?" Sometimes it is the stigma within the very organizations meant to help people that perpetuate stereotypes. At another time, a staff person said this about a CDI peer working with the facilities department. "He was walking around talking to himself when no one was around! Are you sure he's safe?" All CDIs had a job coach, so the question should have been, "Is he doing his job well?" He was. He just talked to himself. I talk to myself sometimes.

> Sometimes it is the stigma within the very organizations meant to help people that perpetuate stereotypes.

In essence, it is the value base of an organization that defines its culture, or "the way things are done around here." The various processes of an organization, managerial as well as clinical processes, are connected to the mission and ultimately to vision by its values. By anchoring oneself to a value base, the leader ensures that processes aimed at achieving the organization's mission must pass through the "value funnel." By funneling processes, whether new processes or old, through its values an organization attains congruence, consistency, and sense of direction.

Senge writes about the importance of values in his seminal work, *The Fifth Discipline: The Art and Practice of the Learning Organization* (Senge, 2006). He said that "...core values are necessary to help people with day-to-day decision making" (p. 208). As contrasted with values; purpose, mission, and vision may be too abstract or long term. Senge says, with regard to core organizational values that: "People need guiding stars to navigate and make decisions day to day. Core values are only helpful if they can be translated into concrete behaviors" (p. 209).

> By anchoring oneself to a value base, the leader ensures that processes aimed at achieving the organization's mission must pass through the "value funnel."

4

Leaders create an organizational structure and culture that empowers their employees and themselves.

- The leader sees staff as investments and assets rather than simply costs.

- The leader delegates power and authority to the employees.

- The leader ensures the staff have access to the information they need.

- The leader models how to process information.

- The leader encourages employees to think about their jobs and not just do the job.

- The leader recognizes staff who act in a empowered way.

- The leader encourages staff to develop their own opportunities— to stretch their abilities and to risk.

- The leader eliminates organizational traditions that hinder empowerment.

- The leader encourages staff to work smarter—not just harder.

- The leader recognizes employees for their outside-of-work activities.

- Leaders choose and retain staff that embody the organization's values.

- Leaders take time to reflect on their own leadership.

- Leaders access mentors who provide the leader with honest feedback, unique perspectives, and new information.

Leaders create an organizational structure and culture that empowers their employees and themselves.

Behind every good leader is another good leader.

—*William A. Anthony*

The fabled coach of the Boston Celtics, Red Auerbach, was successful in creating leaders. Many of the players on his team chose and were chosen to become the head coaches for other teams. Was this a statistical aberration? We think not. Emerging leaders are, most commonly, part of an organizational structure that supports the development of leadership qualities in their employees. Internal leadership cannot develop without an opportunity for employees to feel empowered, mentored, and supported by their supervisors.

Like Red Auerbach, Elizabeth Childs was also a leader in Massachusetts, though in a different venue. Elizabeth encouraged her staff to think with her and to help her process information.

> People in my position just cannot do these jobs alone, it's just not possible nor do we have all the answers; even the best leaders are not smart enough to have all the answers. If you can create a team where there is safe room for disagreement, resolution, problem solving, vigorous debate, vigorous conversations; then together I think you often, collectively, come to the best decision you could possibly make in a situation—even though it actually may not be what anyone on their own would have thought was the right decision. I think the leadership team has to be in a place where they already share a vision for the organization—this is crit-

ical. You must create a team where I, as a leader, can present issues, hear the debate back and forth, and hear everyone's point of view. It does not mean that you get consensus. In fact, I think a lot of times you do not, but you get really good ideas that I, as the leader of the organization, can use well to make the final decision. Through this process, it is always clear to me which decision is the best one and what the consequences are, whatever decision I'm going to make.

An organization that empowers its employees views employees as an asset rather than as a cost. Far too many mental health organizations fail to realize that their staff, while being their major expense, are also their major advantage. Winning organizations are created by employees who are empowered by their leaders. Such employees think of themselves as the primary asset of the organization—and they act accordingly. Nevada's Carlos Brandenburg reinforced this principle.

> An organization that empowers its employees views employees as an asset rather than as a cost.

I think that the issue of empowerment is extremely important because you need to surround yourself with individuals who feel that they have not only the responsibility, but the authority. That's one of the things that I've always been able to do. I really believe in not only the empowerment of staff, but the empowerment of consumers, and staff who are themselves consumers. We basically now have over 20 consumers working for us in a variety of clinical settings. They are working in the ACT programs, with inpatients, and in outpatient clinics as staff members. They themselves then are empowered. They interact with other consumers who see these folks being hired and they set a very positive role model. They model recovery. It also was very important for me to model this, in my own office, because I was always trying to get folks in the community to hire consumers of services. It was hard for me to go to Wal-Mart or J.C. Penny's or where ever and advocate for them to hire consumers when I wasn't hiring them myself.

Carlos went on:

> Let me give you another example. We are now one of the states
> that pretty much has integrated their electronic medical records.
> All of my clinics and all of my hospitals are using electronic med-
> ical records. I can have a consumer that is from a remote area of
> rural Nevada go to Las Vegas and walk into a clinic and say I am
> such and such from this clinic and I'm out of my medication. They
> can go on our electronic medical records and get the information
> and prescribe the medication that he was receiving when he at his
> home site. What I ended up doing, to make this happen, was to
> meet with one of my management information staff who is very,
> very good and basically said to him, "I want you to develop for
> me this electronic medical record system." I gave him not only
> the authority, but I gave him the responsibility. It was his—I
> stayed out of it. I empowered him. I think that approach worked
> and went a great way in helping to him to succeed. Every once in
> awhile, he would want me to send out a memo under my signa-
> ture to my agency directors, which I would, to facilitate a process
> or a training schedule or something. But mostly he was empow-
> ered to do what needed to be done. I think staff's ability and the
> power afforded to the employee are extremely important. I now
> have pretty much an integrated management information system
> for the inpatient units, the outpatient units, my billing services,
> and the pharmacy.

Sal Barbara, CEO of Atlantic Shores (now GEO Care, Inc.)/South
Florida State Hospital, also facilitated opportunities for his staff to
be empowered. He pulled his leadership team together when he
made the decision to improve the safety of persons served by
reducing seclusion and restraint. Sal, who did not have a clinical
background, had the foresight to empower his team to do "whatever it takes" to make the necessary changes in hospital operations. Two members of this team were people in recovery who
were employed in paid positions. These consumer/peer leaders,
along with the rest of that team, developed and implemented a
plan to reduce violence that included significantly improving daily
off-unit treatment choices; reviewing, revising, or discontinuing
many unit rules linked to enforcement that led to conflict and vio-

lence between staff and residents; and enlisting the assistance of peer staff to debrief staff and residents involved in seclusion and restraint events so that the information on event antecedents could be used to inform further operational changes (Huckshorn, 2001).

In Oklahoma, Terry Cline made certain that staff saw themselves as the most important components of the organization.

> From the very beginning of an employee's hire we talk about the importance of what they do. I go to every one of those new employee orientations, and I talk about the significance of their contribution to this agency. I also talk about the fact that they may be in an administrative role and may never work with anyone directly who has used services, but each of these roles are critical to the functioning of the department, otherwise we wouldn't have that position there. I talk about how tight the dollars are and that we would not be funding their position if it was not critical toward achieving our mission.

Terry also made sure that staff had access to information they need through weekly meetings with his leadership staff. This time also was used to reinforce the point that staff had a life outside the organization, and that these family and community activities were also important.

> We have a formalized leadership meeting once a week, as well as an offsite breakfast meeting once a week where we go for coffee. Typically, we do talk about work, but we also talk about going to the lake and vacations and other things that somehow make us more human and connected with one another. So we have a better sense of what's going on with each other and can help support each other again in a way that's more personalized. Having that meeting offsite, religiously on Thursday mornings at 7:30, has paid great dividends for our group. We emphasize that we're not an agency that's built on fancy equipment and big beautiful buildings. We invest in people because people are the vehicles for change, and again, no matter what your job is, you are critical to

> We invest in people because people are the vehicles for change, and again, no matter what your job is, you are critical to the end result.

the end result, which feeds directly back to our mission of promoting Healthy Communities in Oklahoma.

At Elgin State Hospital in Illinois, Raul Almazar, like Terry Cline, made sure staff understood how their job contributed to the organization from day one.

Because of our focus on recovery, every employee who gets hired is asked to write a personal vision statement of how they can assist in helping people to recover in their specific role. When you have a dietary staff member that says, "my mission is to serve three good meals a day to help people recover"; that brought tears to our eyes. And another thing about our vision, as we progressed, we ended up training all 700 people. We realized that we needed to also train our non-clinical staff. My driver has to know the principles and so does housekeeping and dietary. We provide a four-hour training for all of these staff. And the payoff has been phenomenal for both consumers and staff.

> When you have a dietary staff member that says, "my mission is to serve three good meals a day to help people recover"; that brought tears to our eyes.

Bob Williams, the superintendent of Florida State Hospital when he was interviewed, saw his staff as a resource that needed to be empowered. Within a year after arrival, he developed a list of about 50 people within the organization who had significant leadership potential, but were not typically in leadership positions. Bob went to this list when job positions opened up. "We didn't get very hung up on credentials." In essence, he looked for certain characteristics in people, such as their ability to relate to residents as individuals, to their willingness to work hard, and to their desire to lead. "The educational degree was one of least important criteria." This is the group in which Bob invested his training resources. Bob made sure that these employees understood their value to the organization. "I told them up front that they were the critical ingredients toward creating a successful hospital. They were there to be change agents. They had my personal support." Several years later, Bob estimated that at least three quarters of this group of would-be leaders became leaders in their own right.

Many of the leaders we interviewed spoke about their "leadership team." The team members became empowered in a number of ways, including their selection by the leader, their mandate from the leader, and/or their experiences seeing the leader up close in a leadership capacity. Unfortunately, if the team is not aligned with the vision and values, there is real danger that the team is a team in name only. "Real leadership teams" are a group of talented people working for a cause that is bigger than each of them individually. It is only when that unifying cause is present that teams can outperform individuals. Elizabeth Childs spoke about her team allowing her to make decisions she would otherwise not have been able to make as effectively. Sal Barbara demonstrated what can happen when the leader empowers competent staff and then basically gets out of way except in a supportive role. Terry Cline talked to every new employee about their contribution to the agency's mission. Bob Williams made sure his team understood their value to the organization. Each of these leaders was trying to align each team member to the larger good toward which everyone played a part. Later on in this chapter you will read how Gene Johnson kept his teams aligned in part through performance goals and Elizabeth Childs through embracing common values.

> "Real leadership teams" are a group of talented people working for a cause that is bigger than each of them individually. It is only when that unifying cause is present that teams can outperform individuals.

> Individual employees who feel empowered think in a very different way than their disempowered colleagues.

Individual employees who feel empowered think in a very different way than their disempowered colleagues. Empowered employees are not just conditioned to respond in certain ways. They see their job as not just a job to do, but as a job to think about. They are not just conditioned to respond to a task, but they also analyze it, refine it, and maybe even eliminate it.

In Arkansas, Larry Miller gave medical staff opportunities to think about their jobs in different ways.

> I want you to step back from what you do every day and think about an area that you've been really interested in, or that really bugs you, or what is really distinct to your unit. Think about what

you might do to study that a little bit more. Obviously, I wanted them to continue to see their primary work as important, but I also wanted them to grow. They all looked at me like "what? You want us to do what? You want us to think differently; you want us to do something different?" I said, "Yes, I think that would be important to all of you in your careers; most of you are fairly young." And some of them actually took me seriously and went on and began to think about their personal career goals, and they'd come back and they'd meet with me for support regarding their personal needs and work interests. I also said to them that we've got to find time for you to do this. This can't just be an add-on.

Empowered employees don't simply work longer hours—although many do. It is not that they just work hard. They also work smarter. Long hours are not the foundation for empowerment. Effective leadership empowers employees by ensuring that they have access to the information they need—an important component of empowerment. Scott Graham, who was the CEO of two highly successful organizations, first in Florida and then in Maryland, spoke strongly during his interview on the importance of empowered employees. He envisioned himself as a "consultant to his staff," making sure they had the information to be successful. He believed that as a leader, it was his job to make sure his staff "had the tools to do their job, a guiding framework provided by the mission and values, and then to get out of their way."

> He believed that as a leader, it was his job to make sure his staff "had the tools to do their job, a guiding framework provided by the mission and values, and then to get out of their way."

Organizational leadership not only ensures that the organization's structure allows the employees to get the information they need. Effective leaders also assure that employees have the requisite skills to make use of the information they receive. As described in the next chapter on human technology, employees can learn various skill sets that help them use this kind of information more powerfully.

Empowered employees are not expected to simply make simple, rote, conditioned responses to the information that they obtain. They are expected to explore, understand, and act on the information. By using thinking and decision-making skills they can work with the information to come up with new goals and tasks. By processing the information employees come up with the next idea. If they don't process information, then they generally will just implement the last idea rather than the next new idea.

Gene Johnson of META Services in Phoenix talked about the importance of giving his staff the opportunities and supports to stretch their abilities and to work smarter.

> As the CEO and the organizational leader, my desire is to develop and support us to be an "empowered organization." To me this means that, much like an individual in his or her personal recovery, each employee in the organization is continuously learning and growing. So my job is to delegate as much as each employee/team can take on. This is based in the belief that each employee/team has assets, value, and strengths. They can perform and create extraordinary results. I believe in them. The employee's job is to take responsibility (being the source of the results) and be fully accountable (owning the results, whatever they are). Then my task as a leader is to make available the resources and supports to the employee/team so they can be successful with what they are creating. This is the organization empowerment model we practice. This sounds like recovery to me.

Much like an individual in his or her personal recovery, each employee in the organization is continuously learning and growing.

> One example of this is an initiative we called "Project Empowerment" (PE). Several years ago, in our 24/7 crisis inpatient unit, there was a lack of continuity from shift to shift with an absence of leadership. One day I called the unit, trying to find out the status of a specific client, and no one would help and no one could tell me who was in charge. So, still learning about this empowerment approach, I began the new "PE" initiative. I asked that teams form. Employees shuffled around and rearranged schedules because to be a team required that each team always had to have the same type of employees. One team was responsible for days, the front half of the week, and another the back half of the week. We created four teams that covered all days, 24/7, in each center.

Then I asked that they designate a team leader. I didn't care what their discipline was, but the team leaders had to have leadership ability. They were to be the on-line point for their team and present their team results in our monthly "PE" meetings. They got paid a bit more to take on this additional responsibility. Then together, we set performance goals and thresholds in key areas. We rewarded and bonused teams each quarter that were meeting or exceeding performance thresholds. Through delegation, the teams were empowered to create exemplary results. The methods were up to them. They were provided tools to track and measure their results, and leadership was available to provide support, but they had to own what results they created. We saw some teams make extraordinary progress; others seemed to go up and down, while a couple just couldn't seem to make much progress. But in spite of the varied results from team to team, our organizational culture, values, and attitudes shifted as employees became more empowered.

> By developing an organizational structure that allows and prepares employees to create, the leader actually becomes more powerful rather than less powerful.

The more people in the organization who possess the necessary information to do their jobs and know how to use the information to generate new ideas, the better off the organization will be, and the better off its leadership will be. Leaders understand that by giving power away, the leader gains more power. Leaders understand that the next source of creative ideas usually come from the staff who are closest to the task. By developing an organizational structure that allows and prepares employees to create, the leader actually becomes more powerful rather than less powerful.

Along these lines, Paolo del Vecchio of the Office of Consumer Affairs at SAMSHA stated that:

By empowering others, we empower ourselves. One of the first principles of the consumer movement is defined as "empowering others," and that includes staff we supervise. An example of that occurred when we were trying to develop a statewide consumer voice in New Mexico. We were at a retreat site in a small, rural town with a group of about 30 people. It was cold sitting around a camp fire. We were talking with some of the consumers there, who were trying to have their voices heard, and one of the participants, a relative newcomer, announced something like, "I'm going to try. I'm going to try and go out there and work in my local community to make sure consumers have jobs. Peers must support recovery." He was demonstrating a leadership behavior in doing this; I knew that I had helped to plant that seed somehow within him, and this solidified my belief that I could make a difference by empowering others. This particular person went on to touch many people in the recovery work that we do.

One of the factors contributing to the fad of reengineering in the 1990s was the leader/manger's reluctance to reduce their authority. Authoritarian leaders were more apt to embrace the idea of "get it right and keep it going" rather than the idea of "get it right and make it better, and better, and better" or even "make it something else." (Hammer & Champy, 1993). On the flip side, however, leaders cannot empower others by disempowering themselves. They need to model how they themselves are accessing information and processing it to come up with new ideas. Leaders who themselves don't have "thinking skills" (Carkhuff & Berenson, 2000a) are by their very nature disempowered. Unfortunately, the employees of these leaders who display thinking skills are seen often as a threat— and in the supposed interest of management control, the disempowered leader restricts opportunities for other leaders to emerge. In so doing, the leadership creates an organizational structure and ideology that can not and will not empower their employees and will squelch meaningful mentoring of potential leaders.

> Authoritarian leaders were more apt to embrace the idea of "get it right and keep it going" rather than the idea of "get it right and make it better, and better, and better..."

Outstanding leaders can create an organizational structure and culture that empowers their employees in many different ways. Good intentions are simply not enough. Certain leadership behaviors and organizational supports are needed. One simple leadership act that creates an organizational culture is to think out loud with one's staff. In other words, leaders don't always process information in isolation from their staff. Besides modeling what you expect employees to do, leaders who "think out loud" with their staff also may find that their staff creates innovations for them to consider. In many instances, the creative ideas come, not from the designated leaders, but from their staff. Leaders who think along with their staff increase the possibility of coming up with a variety of creative ideas.

When Pablo Hernandez was director of Wyoming State Hospital, he stressed the importance of modeling to his staff how he did his work, so that eventually they could do his job.

> I want people to take my job. I understand succession planning. I train people to take my job, continuously. I call people to my office daily, so they hear me in conference calls, they hear me dictating letters to so and so, etc., and I hope they see me as kind of a role model. I mention their contributions to my executive leadership. I say things like, you know, I had Paul, and I had Roger, and I had Ellen in my office and we did A, B, C together. The staff has taken over many, many, many functions that I used to execute, even to the point of producing the documents. I don't produce the documents anymore. I say to them, I will work with them; but they produce the documents; they filter that work through me; we work together and they produce it. I am talking about empowerment constantly moving down through the organization. So then it becomes embedded. Now I don't have to worry about a judge calling me and saying to me, "Pablo, you are not taking my patients." I will reply, "your honor, when you're having a problem in your county about a person and the person is a forensic person, please do not call me. Call so and so; she has the control to manage this problem." And you know what? That has not disempowered me at all, to the contrary. The staff has embraced even further responsibility, and I have not given a single one of them a salary increase either! They're doing it and they feel empowered. Staff empowerment eliminates the unnecessary thought about what's going to come here when Pablo's through. So I'm preparing the leadership for my absence; they are the future; eventually I will be the past. A leader needs to look at how will this work be sustained; how do I empower; how do we

> I'm preparing the leadership for my absence; they are the future; eventually I will be the past.

say that what we have created here for consumers will continue in the future in this organization?

Judy Trysnicki was an example of a leader who created conditions that empowered her employees. When Judy was interviewed, she was president of Housing Options Made Easy, Inc. (HOME), a nonprofit corporation that she and other people with psychiatric disabilities founded to assist people to obtain and retain affordable and acceptable housing. Within four years, HOME's budget had increased over 1,000 percent, and HOME was providing their clientele with 161 rental stipends a month, plus peer advocacy, self-help, start-up apartment furniture, and transportation assistance. Judy said, "I think out loud with staff and engage my entire staff in problem solving critical issues." As an indicator of her efforts in fostering an empowerment culture, she created a new tradition whereby the chairperson for staff meetings was rotated through all her staff. To ensure that staff had the up-to-date information and contacts that they needed to act in an empowered way, staff regularly attended housing conferences. Judy stated emphatically, "we don't want people to look at us differently, but as contributing members of society."

In Delaware, Renata Henry spoke about how she tried to support her senior leadership staff to grow and further develop themselves, but to keep her informed of what they are learning.

I encourage people to do their thing. They need to be active on a national level. They need to be active professionally. They need to keep their training up. They need to learn how to be able to run good meetings. Good leaders are able to unify the people who report to them. You need to encourage them to grow. My main rule is that I don't want any surprises. You have got to communicate information, so I know what's out there. Not to say if it's right or wrong, but just to be aware of it because, especially in a small state, I just don't want any surprises. I don't want to go anywhere and hear something that you haven't already told me. Sure I'm going to hear things that you may not have been aware of, but I don't want to hear anything that you're aware of that I don't know.

Leaders encourage staff to develop their own opportunities—to stretch their abilities—to assume risk. A leader ensures this by putting employees in positions that stretch them, or by putting them in touch with people who push them. Leaders who encourage their staff to stretch cannot constantly second guess their ideas or the staff will contract faster than a rubber band. Judy Trysnicki commented that her staff were somewhat immobilized by the fear of making a mistake. She reframed the notion of mistake into a "learning opportunity," so that her staff would not be afraid to develop new ideas.

> Leaders encourage staff to develop their own opportunities— to stretch their abilities— to assume risk.

Cheryl Gagne at the Boston University Center for Psychiatric Rehabilitation's services division stressed the importance of employee growth.

Staff are encouraged to build upon their strengths. We have organized many courses and activities that enable individuals to shine. For a human service agency, we have invested a lot of time and other resources to increase the knowledge, skill, and satisfaction of individual staff members. Staff are encouraged to take courses at Boston University and always are given release time to do so. Staff also are asked to attend and present at conferences so that they're able to connect with other professionals. I cannot recall a time when a staff person requested to take a course or attend a conference and permission was not granted, even when the content of the course or conference didn't have a direct connection to their current project. We try to be forward thinking and imagine that the course or conference will enhance the overall knowledge base at the Center. Staff often are asked to take on responsibilities (with lots of support) that they have not done before. In a way, we have a growth plan for every staff person. If a staff person in the services division wants to explore his or her interest in research, he or she will be given a role in a research project. Likewise, if someone wants to test his or her competence in training, he or she will be given some training tasks. Staff also are supported in strengthening their clinical skills.

> Staff are encouraged to build upon their strengths.

Many staff participate in therapy outside of the Center in an effort to improve their empathy and responsiveness to students. Staff supervision also focuses on the development of clinical skills. Self-care is explicitly supported. At lunchtime, staff are encouraged to go for a run, a swim, a sauna, etc. There are Tai Chi and Yoga classes offered at the Center that staff can take. Staff self-care is built into the structure of the services program, and we try to exemplify self-care for the people to whom we are providing services.

Employees feel empowered when they think they count. Leaders who only count the bottom line will have difficulty developing empowered employees. Employees must see the leader as driven by goals other than the bottom line. The leaders' decisions also must reflect staff growth and development.

Leaders must specifically encourage their staff to think about their jobs. The key word here is specifically. It is not enough to imply that this activity is happening. Organizations typically become more excited about a new building than an employee's new idea. Empowered employees must feel more valued than a new building. Thinking and reflecting on one's job is something not often done, unless the leadership directly encourages and supports it.

> Employees feel empowered when they think they count.

Judi Chamberlin, who became an internationally acclaimed consultant, reflected on her leadership in empowering the members of a consumer-operated service. Judi delegated power to the membership, ensured that her staff had access to the needed information, and modeled how to process the information.

The Ruby Rogers Center had the value that everyone (whether paid staff or not, all were members) had something of value to contribute and that everyone's participation was important. This value was institutionalized through the weekly business meeting where decisions were made. I made available to the members, through the business meeting, basic organizational documents, such as our contract with the Department of Mental Health and the budget, and helped members to read and understand these documents. Because most members lived on benefits, they had little idea of what went into structuring an organizational budget.

When they first heard that the organization had an annual budget in excess of $100,000, many members responded by saying that we had plenty of money to fund all kinds of non-essential spending. Many meetings were spent reviewing the budget and showing how nearly all of it was devoted to fixed costs: rent, salaries, insurance, food, etc. Eventually members were able to appreciate the relatively small amount of the budget that could support discretionary spending, and were able to decide collectively how to spend these funds.

As described so far in this book, leaders inspire people with their vision, guide with their values, and free staff to initiate action by centralizing their mission while decentralizing their operations. In addition, as focused on in this chapter, leaders need to immerse their employees in an organizational culture and structure that directly supports their empowerment.

Kim Ingram of Thomasville, Alabama did just that. Kim recounted how this principle of empowerment can make leaders and staff apprehensive, but if the hospital environment wants to facilitate patient empowerment then it must facilitate staff empowerment as well. Kim stated that, at one time, all senior staff at the state hospital reported to the director, rather than working out issues between themselves. This culture had to change. Kim believed that the leader must encourage staff to make important decisions and then not "beat them up" about the decisions that were made. Kim understood that, while staff did not always make the decision she would have made, they could all live with these. Kim also learned that the most senior clinicians are not always the best leaders, and she gave some of them the opportunity to return to being a full-time clinician.

> Leaders need to immerse their employees in an organizational culture and structure that directly supports their empowerment.

> The leadership team was involved in setting the vision and values and then was expected to get out of the way of an empowered staff. Some clinician/leaders simply could not do that.

In yet another example, Kim recalled that the new rehabilitation director wanted to develop a rehabilitation initiative in a way Kim would not have done. Kim talked to her about it, and then gave her a shot at implementing it. Kim made sure she had the resources to do it, and got out of her way. However, "some staff pitched a fit." She let the staff know that she supported the direction of the new rehabilitation director. Kim stated proudly that it became an excellent rehabilitation program.

Leadership also must understand the importance of diversity and non-work expertise in their staff. Employees who are recognized in the organizational culture for outside-of-work activities feel more important, and possibly more empowered. Be they an excellent cook, coach, cellist or whatever, an empowering organizational culture values these contributions and diversity in their employees.

One aspect of the organization's structure that impedes empowerment are those routines which do not serve the key values of an organization. Many activities of an organization are done out of traditions that are no longer relevant. Staff cannot become empowered when they are doing tasks which are not fundamental to the organization's values, mission, and vision. Leadership must routinely examine meetings, rules, regulations, clinical practices, memos, procedures, and entire programs to see if they are relevant. If not, they should be quickly discarded. This "examination" of an organization's fundamental processes takes work and requires a level of involvement by staff that is empowered to act and understand the goal. Many mental health service settings are unable to move forward in this way because leaders have become so disengaged from the important daily operational decisions made in their setting and/or because leaders do not make the effort to find out what is occurring.

> Leadership must also understand the importance of diversity and non-work expertise in their staff.

Renata Henry was very specific with her staff about re-examining organizational traditions.

> I remember telling my staff that when I ask, "why are we doing something a certain way," that an unacceptable answer was, "because that's the way we've always done it." I wanted to know why and the rationale behind it; that it did not matter if I thought

it made sense or not, but that I wanted their reason. I wanted all of the staff to start thinking about, "why do we do this?" I was trying to lay the groundwork to challenge the status quo.

According to Kouzes and Posner (1995), the organization's culture should allow employees to work on something that lets them feel good about themselves, learn something worthwhile, learn new things, develop new skills, experience freedom in one's job, and do things that one does best. Each of the above characteristics of a culture is directly a function of the leadership. Judy Trysnicki's organization is an excellent example of a leader creating such a culture. Even though Judy's organization was small, Judy tried to facilitate staff empowerment by matching the staff's job functions to what they liked to do and were best at doing, no matter how relatively simple the task seemed. Judy illustrated this point with the following comment.

> The organization's culture should allow employees to work on something that lets them feel good about themselves, learn something worthwhile, learn new things, develop new skills, experience freedom in one's job, and do things that one does best.

> For example, a person who was doing paperwork only, but who had good phone skills, might be switched to the phone, while a person working on the computer might be switched to office work.

Judy also made sure her staff had the opportunity to learn something worthwhile, "as varied as from grant writing to keyboarding."

In addition to feeling empowered by using one's skills, employees feel empowered when they work in an organization of people with like-minded values. Leaders choose and retain staff that embody the organization's values. Elizabeth Childs of Massachusetts was very specific on this point.

> I feel very strongly that you must choose your team based on values, too. Most important to me is that my senior team members embrace and adopt values that I think are consistent with the organization's mission. Frankly, almost everyone I hire, even if they are not the best performer or don't do their job perfectly, if they have the right values, you can usually work with them pretty intensively to get them to a good place and performance. More

difficult are the people who do not have the values but do get things done. It's hard for me to say, sometimes, "you're not on my team and not performing adequately because you do not share the organization's values." There is often a lot of pressure to keep someone because it looks like they're doing a good job. Our human resource policies are not set up to support making decisions about people's performance and longevity based on their values. So I think sometimes it's very difficult to negotiate and hang on to what you really believe are important values in terms of delivery of services. However, creating a team that shares your values and doing it well is critical to the effective leader of an organization.

When staff act in an empowered way, it is important for the leader to recognize such activity. They can recognize the results of this empowerment in a number of ways. For example, they might send out congratulatory memos and letters. They might celebrate success by means of public rewards and recognition events. Leaders can be the cheerleaders at public events. If that is too difficult a role for the leader, they must ensure that someone is acting in the role of cheerleader. An example of this was Gayle Bluebird's work at South Florida State Hospital. In the midst of attempting to receive JCAHO accreditation for the first time, move into a new hospital, start up a treatment mall, and reduce the use of seclusion and restraint, the leadership team, including Gayle, knew that staff who demonstrated best practices had to be recognized for their incredible work in changing this hospital's culture. Many ideas were initiated, such as providing more convenient parking spaces, recognition by the CEO in a formal certificate, and memos for personnel files. But Gayle Bluebird, a peer hired in a paid staff role came up with the best plan. The plan was to interview hospital residents and gather information from them on what, specifically, hospital staff had done to help these residents to "get better." This amazingly powerful project resulted in a published document titled "Good Stories" that contained many vignettes from service users on who, why, and how they had been helped to move

> When staff act in an empowered way, it is important for the leader to recognize such activity.

toward recovery, naming specific staff members. The document was disseminated during annual nurse's week and had a huge impact on the staff named as helping, and conversely, a different kind of impact on staff who were not named. Gayle understood the power of recognition and went to the most important information source: the service users.

The leaders who were interviewed for this book were universal in their praise for their employees. Most stated without any prompting that without key staff their mission would not have been accomplished. By giving credit, leaders get credit and credibility—but by taking credit, leaders lose their credit over time as most mental health professionals are very aware of the work that is done by middle management and direct care staff and realize that no significant change occurs in an agency without the buy-in by direct care staff and middle management.

> The leaders who were interviewed for this book were universal in their praise for their employees.

However, it is not just the leader's staff that helps the leader to function effectively. Leaders also must take the time to empower themselves. At times this may be networking with persons in similar leadership positions. Larry Miller articulated this very point.

> I really value the medical director's conferences at the National Association of State Mental Health Program Directors (NASMHPD). I also work with the American Psychiatric Association because those kinds of things keep me stimulated by talking to other people. As much as I want to get my staff out in the field and other places, I need to do that as well.

At other times, leaders become more empowered in their roles by taking the time to reflect on their own leadership. During Paolo del Vecchio's interview, he took the time to think about his own development as a leader.

> I think I was chosen to do this work, first, by having that personal experience with mental illness. Also important was discovering how you can be empowered, yourself, by joining together with others who have similar personal experiences. I worked with Joe Rogers for 5 or 6 years. He taught me a lot. Then I worked for the

City of Philadelphia Office of Mental Health in planning and policy making. This particular position was created in 1995 and was partly created by the direct action of consumers. CMHS used to have a service system improvement grant for states to support statewide consumer activities primarily. We, many of us consumers, attended their annual conference in 1994. A group of consumers, about 20 of us, were unhappy that there was insufficient consumer voice at this meeting. So we took it in our own hands and walked across the parking lot to the offices of then CMHS director, Bernie Arons. We proceeded to hold a "sit in" in the administrative offices. Dr. Arons met with us and heard our concerns, and that was one driver that I believed helped to push the agency to craft a position announcement for a consumer affairs director, as well as pushing several state mental health associations to develop Offices of Consumer Affairs. I applied for this job at SAMHSA and got it. I think that my involvement in the consumer movement for over 20 years has been rewarding; how many opportunities does one have to love what they do and to help inspire others to action?

Kathryn Power said she believed that leadership is a lifelong learning experience.

I started to understand that I had to cultivate my own philosophy of leadership. Anyone who says that they've finished looking at leadership and understands it completely doesn't know who they are. You have to be a student of leadership throughout your life. I think you have to cultivate a sense of curiosity and inquiry as a foundation of leadership. If you don't have a sense of inquiry and you don't aggressively pursue that, then I think you have stopped being a student of leadership and are not being honest with yourself as a leader. I think it is very important that people need to really understand that leaders need the time to step back, be content to sort through things on their own, sort through any problems as an individual, and then use others around them to help them further the developmental work that's necessary. I think there's a lot of introspection that is important in leadership, and particularly, in transformational leadership.

Some leaders commented that the very task of contributing to this leadership book gave them an opportunity for this needed reflection on their own leadership development. Larry Miller said:

> This interview and preparing for it is the kind of activity that gives you a chance to think differently. I always need to sit back and think—which is one of the things that I find fun. It's different than the projects you have to do everyday.

Renata Henry remarked directly to us in a similar fashion.

> This process gave me an opportunity to think about leadership again, because on a day-to-day basis, I don't think we think about it. But an opportunity like this to talk about it—I would hope is valuable for all the people that you interview because it gives them a time in their busy calendar to stop and think about the issue of leadership.

Rupert Goetz from Hawaii echoed these sentiments. Rupert noted that leaders need to be "lifelong learners" and constantly question their knowledge base in order to move it forward and eliminate outdated practices that do not lead to desired outcomes, no matter how politically difficult that might be. At the conclusion of his interview, Pablo Hernandez took a moment to reflect on the fundamentals of leadership.

> The learnings that I have had in 40 years of public mental health in the United States—they have come from being able to listen to the recipients of services. Many years ago we called them patients, and now we name them clients and consumers. You know, my eyes and my ears really have changed. They did not teach me any of this in school. I have learned from my colleagues, my friends, and especially from the people that I have helped to serve. It is the clients, the consumers, who have touched me the most, and their families. My own internal shift of culture, my own vision has changed because my eyes were opened and my ears were unplugged by them, and then my mouth began to articulate their language, a language that was initially foreign to me, but now a language that then became more of what was relevant.

Leaders also may use mentors themselves who provide leaders with honest feedback, unique perspectives, and new information. Elizabeth Childs of Massachusetts remarked about this aspect of leadership.

> One of the things I would say about being a leader—you need a person, a mentor, or mentors with whom you can be very vulnerable. You need to be able to have people to whom you can talk with total honesty about what you're doing, and who aren't afraid to make you confront your own mistakes. I think it is hard to find those people in a place that is safe for you to talk. This is a major issue. I actually have sought out the very senior people who are, for the most part, retired but who have had tremendous experience in leadership with mental health care in various different venues who have perspectives; people who I've been able to trust personally and be very vulnerable and honest with about my own decisions and mistakes. And to speak about things that even people on my own team don't know; things that I wish I hadn't done. You've got to have somebody who can help you work through what decision you made and how it could have been different or better.
>
> If a leader does not confront what they did wrong, at least to themselves, you do not learn from your mistakes. This is not about public confession. You have to confront what you did wrong because then you can learn and do it better the next time. I think if you're really going to espouse an organization that is always learning and growing and have a culture of continuous quality improvement, then you have to live that. You can't just pay lip service to it; you have to live it yourself. It's like your own quality check. I have a person I see very regularly who is very good, who was in the state hospital system for a number of years, ran big agencies, and is now retired. I've seen this person probably about twice a month and have been able to bounce real operational stuff and issues off this person. I also have two or three other people I talk to on a regular basis. I talk to all of these people to work through decisions I have made that I have second guessed later; decisions that I thought did not fit with my ideal of what kind of leader I want to be. And I could talk to at least one

of them about why, and understand it, and get clear within myself why I did what I did. It's been very helpful to me. These mentors are not afraid to confront me, and in a kind and gentle way, help me to understand what did not fit with my overall values. Sometimes the reason is that the situation just happened too fast; I hadn't had a chance to think it through; others, I just did not clearly understand at the time of the decision. In any case, having a mentor is imperative for anyone in a leadership position.

In essence, in an organizational culture that promotes individual empowerment, leaders structure the organization in a way that they themselves are empowered. Very often they will find that they are empowered and pushed along by their followers—like a stiff wind on their backs. And if such followers are equipped with the human technology that they need to do their job at the highest level (see next chapter), the wind at the back of the leader will seen to be at hurricane strength! As it should be, empowered followers will at times lead their leaders. Empowered followers are a vital source of power for their leaders as the leaders work to develop effective organizations.

> As it should be, empowered followers will at times lead their leaders.

5

Leaders ensure that staff are trained in a human technology that can translate vision into reality.

- The leader creates an organizational culture that recognizes the value of a human technology.

- The leader understands the distinction between exposing staff to knowledge and having staff become expert in using the knowledge.

- The leader believes that staff training must focus on skills as well as facts and concepts.

- The leader emphasizes staff expertise as more critical than credentials and roles.

- The leader ensures that the organization's training plan and supervision are linked to the organization's mission.

- The leader ensures that staff are trained to think for themselves and relate skillfully with one another.

- The leader knows that trained staff have less worry about job security.

Leaders ensure that staff are trained in a human technology that can translate vision into reality.

Human technology allows leaders to act more forcefully on their values, to involve staff more fully in the organization's operations, and most importantly, to serve more capably their consumers.

—*William A. Anthony*

Chapter 5 is the second of three chapters that deals with principles related to employees in the leader's organization and reflects the critical importance to principled leaders of staff training, relationships, and staff functioning. Chapter 4 focused on how leaders structure their organizations so that staff are empowered to perform their functions. Chapter 6 will address how leaders relate to their staff in a way that mobilizes staff to do their best work. The leadership principle, described in this chapter, emphasizes how leaders ensure that staff use *human technology* to help close the gap between the organization's vision and current reality. It is this book's least understood principle, as it often is confused with how to go about implementing a typical staff training program. As will become clear in this chapter, ensuring that staff possess effective human technology is a leadership challenge much more difficult than implementing a traditional staff training program.

First of all, we need to understand what is meant by human technology. The generic term "technology" can be thought of as the application of scientific knowledge for the attainment of individual and/or social goals. The phrase, human technology, describes the application of scientific knowledge to achieve *human*

> Human technology, describes the application of scientific knowledge to achieve *human resource goals* rather than industrial or commercial goals.

resource goals rather than industrial or commercial goals (Carkhuff & Berenson, 1976). In a recovery-oriented mental health organization, these human resource goals are related to improving the organization's clinical processes and outcomes, so that increasingly more people have the possibility of recovering from serious mental conditions. Scientific knowledge has accumulated over the last century with respect to how all people, including people with serious mental illnesses, are helped to change and grow (Anthony, 2003; Anthony, Cohen, Farkas & Gagne, 2002; Power, 2005; Onken, Dumont, Ridgeway, Dornan, & Ralph, 2002). The behavioral science literature has identified certain human interactive processes that facilitate growth and development. Primary examples of these processes include:

- People experiencing a positive relationship with the people providing help;

- People being helped to set their own goals;

- People being helped to learn new skills;

- People being helped to plan what steps to take to solve their problems;

- People being inspired to hope; and

- People learning how to manage their own illnesses or symptoms.

In order to engage people with serious mental conditions in the above growth processes, staff in a mental health organization must be skilled in facilitating these processes. For example, to develop a positive relationship with the people they are trying to help, they must possess interpersonal skills. To help people set their own goals, they must be skilled in goal setting. To help people learn new skills, they must possess teaching skills. To help people plan, they must be skilled in thinking or problem-solving skills. To help people hope, they must be skilled in motivational or inspirational skills. These skills are examples of the human technology that leaders must ensure is present in their organizations' practitioners. Leaders ensure that this human technology is stressed in their organization, typically by means of training, reinforcement through supervision and mentoring, and recognition.

Many, if not most, leaders in mental health organizations have a mental health clinical background. Historically, the mental health field has been a field that studies concepts and ideas rather than mastering technologies. Human technology is a set of skills rather than just concepts. Interpersonal skills, teaching skills, and planning skills, like all other types of skills, are mastered through systematic training, practice, and feedback. In contrast, most mental health practitioners studied facts and concepts from books, and were evaluated through written papers and written tests. When the importance of interpersonal skills, teaching skills, and planning skills were included in a clinician's training, they usually were introduced as concepts rather than taught as part of a skills training program.

> Interpersonal skills, teaching skills, and planning skills, like all other types of skills, are mastered through systematic training, practice, and feedback.

As a result, many mental health leaders who have risen to leadership from the clinical ranks, as well as other leaders who don't understand what is meant by a human technology, do not appreciate what their human technology, rightly used, can do for their organization. The idea of training staff in how to relate, how to teach, and how to plan more skillfully is as foreign to these leaders as the thought of training people to be more happy! They have not yet understood that such seemingly subjective traits, such as how to plan better or how to relate better or how to teach better, actually can be taught and measured.

> Many mental health leaders who have risen to leadership from the clinical ranks, as well as other leaders who don't understand what is meant by a human technology, do not appreciate what their human technology, rightly used, can do for their organization.

It is only within this century that the federal leadership in the mental health field has strongly emphasized the need for more skillful practitioners in order to help people with serious mental conditions recover (*Substance Abuse and Mental Health Services Administration News,* 2004). According to this century's first director of SAMHSA's Center for Mental Health Services, Kathryn Power (who readers know about from earlier chapters of this book), "SAMHSA is seeking to introduce a fundamental change in the way mental health services are perceived, accessed, delivered, and financed," she explained.

> Care should focus on facilitating recovery and building resilience—not just managing symptoms. To do this, we must ensure that service providers are taught the *skills* they need to facilitate change. (p. 6)

In a challenge to the leadership of mental health organizations, Power maintains that a major workforce development initiative is needed because:

> Many people in behavioral health care are not being taught the skills they needed to practice safely or effectively...In short we need to educate our workforce to be competent...Our workforce lacks the knowledge, skills, and attitudes necessary to effect the changes we need to make...It will not be enough to educate our workforce in the *theory* [italics added] of competent care. (Power, 2005, p. 489 & 493).

The impact of the knowledge and attitudes that are critical to mental health practice are dramatically reduced if practitioners cannot act skillfully on their attitudes and knowledge. Principled leaders must ensure that they can.

A somewhat similar point was made by Richard Surles, as he reflected on his number of years in public mental health leadership.

> Technologies change. It's not the employees' fault that they may no longer fit in the job. You can't ask people to do things they do not have the skill sets to do; but you can help them get that skill set so that they will be a better fit to do the job. I've always been a great believer that it is the leaders' responsibility to help people adapt; to get the training or find a job that fits a person's skills. In most situations people deserve the training that helps them perform their jobs better.

In some instances, the mantra "Please take your skills and graces to use in other places" is relevant. But only after leadership has made all efforts to bring staff to a place where they have been trained consistent with the new organizational vision, mission, and values.

Fortunately, there are numerous training packages in various human technology areas, such as case management, psychiatric rehabilitation, social skills training, preventing the incidence of conflict and violence, trauma informed care, supported employment, and human resource development that are now available and have been referenced (Anthony, Cohen, Farkas & Gagne, 2002; Canady, 2005; National Executive Training Institutes, 2007; Huckshorn, 2007). These technology packages often include such training aids as audiotapes, videotapes, teaching modules, practice exercises, skill rating forms, and reference handbooks.

Human technology training does attempt to enhance knowledge and improve attitudes as well as increase skills. But this gain in knowledge and attitudes must be expressed in actual behavior change. Changes in practitioner behavior is what differentiates human technology training from most staff training initiatives and is what challenges leaders to achieve in their organization. Knowledge, skills, and attitude change, while significant, are most useful only when these changes result in differences in what staff *do*. Human technology training assures that staff behavior change occurs, and is monitored and supervised in an ongoing manner that is focused on outcomes.

> Human technology training assures that staff behavior change occurs, and is monitored and supervised in an ongoing manner that is focused on outcomes.

King Davis, former commissioner of mental health in Virginia, and at the time of the interview, executive director of the Hogg Foundation in Texas, agreed with the idea that a human technology can translate vision into reality.

> We have tried as much as possible to acculturate this focus on human capital in terms of what we do on a day-to-day basis. We also promote staff development. In the course of developing individual work plans, staff members are asked, along with their supervisors, to identify what new information, knowledge, skills, and techniques staff members need in order to get staff up to grade or up to where they need to be, relative to new knowledge.

The intent is to have the staff become as skilled as possible in terms of their own development. That is, part of our mission is not just to develop the organization as a whole, but to be specific to the needs of the individual staff member.

King continued on to emphasize how staff trained in a human technology reaped the by-product of increased job flexibility and security.

So our intent is to make sure that the employees who are here have career opportunities. Let me give you an example. For probably the last 25 or 30 years, there were no career ladders for program officers at Hogg. Once a person came to the Hogg Foundation as a program officer, they stayed in that category until they retired. People had long tenures here, up to 56 years in some instances. I would hope that with the staff development emphases that we have made, that our staff will feel secure about two things. One, secure about their performance here, but also secure that if they so choose, there are other opportunities in philanthropy or mental health that they will be qualified to apply for.

Raul Almazar and his staff at Elgin State Hospital in Illinois understood that behavior did not change simply by talking about concepts. They used role plays and feedback to learn new behaviors, and they involved their consumers in the learning process.

It was critical for us to address workforce development. We began by taking a cross section of management staff, professional staff, and consumers who still were receiving services. They did the actual work on planning for workforce development. We presented them with basic principles, and they were the ones who decided on training for staff. Out of this process, staff told us they were sick of lectures; they liked role play. So half of our training became role plays. The consumer's were the ones that made training come alive and insisted on the inclusion of consumer points of view.

These new role plays caused some initial problems. One of the things that we ran into was that "staff felt vulnerable." We were (and still are) doing role plays of the appropriate approach vs. the inappropriate approach during training, but staff felt that they were showing their weaknesses to the very consumers for whom they are responsible. This actually became a union battle. We went all the way up to central office, and basically, the only concession I made was we would make sure that in the role plays, staff would not be paired with consumers from their units.

By including consumers in the human technology training, Raul ensured that the training plan would be linked to the organization's mission.

We also changed some of our inservices and included consumers in these events. This worked out very well. What we did was to include consumer presentations. The first piece of the consumer's presentation was to talk about treatment and what helped, in other words, "the turning points in my treatment." They spoke directly to the treatment staff about their treatment here. They told staff how those staff had made a difference in their lives and, "that I am not just here to complain." We had some great role plays where consumers played the parts of staff. We had great times practicing these and what it brought home for staff, especially for the direct care staff, was that the consumers really do see all of the things that go on. So that kind of combination really worked nicely for us.

I opened every training. It didn't matter if it was midnight, I opened the training. The message was that this means a lot to me, and this is where we are going. And people did not leave that training without clearly understanding my commitment.

In this particular chapter, we use as examples of leaders' introduction of two human technologies with which we are most familiar:

- the technology of psychiatric rehabilitation (WA), and

- the technology of seclusion/restraint reduction (KH).

With respect to the technology of psychiatric rehabilitation, the Center for Psychiatric Rehabilitation at Boston University has so far identified and operationally defined more than 70 practitioner skills designed to facilitate people's recovery from severe mental illnesses. The Boston University technology has its roots in the research literature of many fields, such as client-centered psychotherapy, social skills training, educational psychology, and cognitive psychology, and includes among others, the skills of teaching, relating, goal setting, inspiring, and planning (Anthony, Cohen, Farkas & Gagne, 2002).

With respect to the technology of preventing incidents of violence and conflict that lead to successful reductions in seclusion/restraint use, NASMHPD's National Technical Assistance Center has developed a prevention model based on primary, secondary, and tertiary strategies that is supported in the literature and in successful demonstration projects (Huckshorn, 2004; National Executive Training Institutes, 2007). Skills required by staff to successfully implement this model include therapeutic and empathic communication skills, assessment skills, person-driven treatment planning skills, writing skills, developing and implementing safety/crisis plans, effective problem solving, and teaching service users and staff how to work side-by-side to change institutional practices that often act as triggers for conflict (Huckshorn, 2004). Examples of leaders' implementation of a human technology will be illustrated first by psychiatric rehabilitation examples, and then with seclusion/restraint reduction examples, followed by other leaders' thoughts on human technology implementation.

> Many of the mental health leaders interviewed in this text understand that they can impact not only their staff's attitudes and knowledge, but also staff behaviors, such as their interpersonal, teaching, and planning skills—skills that are so necessary to achieve changes in consumer outcomes.

A misconception made by some mental health leaders is the belief that the staff training function in their organization cannot be assessed and held accountable for behavioral outcomes. Similar to their own training as mental health practitioners, mental health leaders may believe that one can only be educated in mental health facts and concepts. This is the "wish and hope" construct where training in knowledge and attitudes occurs and staff behavior change is "wished and hoped for." In contrast, many of the mental health leaders interviewed in this text understand that they can impact not only their staff's attitudes and knowledge, but also staff behaviors, such as their interpersonal, teaching, and planning skills—skills that are so necessary to achieve changes in consumer outcomes. Scott Graham was such a leader.

In both of the psychiatric rehabilitation organizations in which Scott Graham was CEO, he evaluated his staff training initiatives and held his trainers and their trainees accountable for staff behavioral change. Like Kathryn Power, Scott believed that:

> Folks who come into our field don't have the skills to provide rehabilitation services to people with psychiatric disabilities. There has to be some consistent training to give people the technologies that will make them more effective. At Revisions, a psychiatric rehabilitation agency in Maryland, we have a comprehensive staff training program that is broken up into semesters, involving modules in interpersonal skills, teaching skills, medication monitoring, case management, etc. Staff are evaluated on their ability to pass the training modules. If they cannot pass, then they should be thinking about some other type of employment. We have had to give up some time, some resources, and money to make this training happen successfully, but we feel it is an investment, and to not do it would not be fair to them or the people that receive our services.

> An important distinction that mental health leaders must understand is the difference between training programs with respect to the concepts of exposure, experience, expertise, and embedding.

Training staff to be competent was not an afterthought in Scott's organizations, even in times of funding cutbacks. Along these lines Scott emphasized:

> It is my belief that when times are tough and you have even fewer resources, you should be beefing up your training budget and providing more training rather than cutting it.

This is an interesting take on human technology training in a time when the first budget to be cut is often the staff development training budget.

An important distinction that mental health leaders must understand is the difference between training programs with respect to the concepts of exposure, experience, expertise, and embedding. Cohen, Farkas and their colleagues (Cohen, 1989; Farkas & Anthony, 2007; Farkas et al., 2003) have developed a method of categorizing the possible objectives of an organization's training program using the alliterative terms of exposure, experience, expertise, and embedding. A training program that achieves the *exposure* objective increases staff awareness of the need for new skills and attitudes by means of didactic presentations and coursework. A training program classified at the *experience* objective supplements the didactic coursework with supervised fieldwork that is related to the facts and concepts taught in the didactic course material. The *expertise* objective is achieved when skill building practice and feedback are added to the didactic material and fieldwork experience, so that change in staff behavior is the intended outcome, rather than knowledge and attitude change only. At the most advanced training objective, *embedding*, the expertise training program is incorporated into the organization's structure. It is only at the expertise and embedding objectives that one can speak of human technology training. Scott Graham's leadership illustrated an organization that has embedded the expertise training within the organization. The leaders illustrated in this chapter attempted to embed their staff's human technology expertise into the very structure of their organizations.

> The *expertise* objective is achieved when skill building practice and feedback are added to the didactic material and fieldwork experience, so that change in staff behavior, rather than knowledge and attitude change only, is the intended outcome.

> At the most advanced training objective, *embedding,* the expertise training program is incorporated into the organization's structure. It is only at the expertise and embedding objectives that one can speak of human technology training.

Staff who work in mental health organizations clearly need more than facts and concepts in order to interact skillfully with their consumers. Effective and principled leaders understand that their organizational training programs must be geared to help their staff do things differently, rather than just know more interesting facts and concepts about what to do. Effective leaders ensure that the human technology training that staff receive is embedded or incorporated into supervisory expectations, job descriptions, performance evaluations and that this didactic training, if provided from external resources, is integrated into routine organizational policy, procedures, and internal trainings. Staff who have been trained toward an expertise objective can demonstrate their skills by means of audio- or videotapes of their interactions with consumers. Their skill development can be observed, and their new learning measured from pre-training to post-training behaviors. Expert staff, unlike most practitioners who possess only didactic knowledge and fieldwork experience, can demonstrate effectively their ability to perform certain skills well and with apriori outcomes.

Mental health leaders who operate consistent with this human technology principle understand that what most helps people who receive services from their organization are the actions of their employees. The most significant employee factor is not the titles of this staff, nor their credentials, nor their demographics, but their ability to perform certain functions that have been shown to relate to people's outcomes. The performance of these functions are enhanced when the staff member possesses interpersonal skills, teaching skills, planning skills, etc. No matter the title, credential, or role, the employee's impact is facilitated by this focus on human technology by the leadership of the organization.

> The most significant employee factor is not the titles of this staff, nor their credentials, nor their demographics, but their ability to perform certain functions that have been shown to relate to people's outcomes.

Dennis Rice's leadership showed he understood the importance of equipping his staff with effective human technology. When Dennis was interviewed, he was director of Alternatives Unlimited, a nonprofit organization serving people with psychiatric disabilities and/or mental retardation. Like many community organizations, Alternatives Unlimited began with money saved from closing a state hospital. Alternatives Unlimited provided residential, vocational, and transportation services to over 400 people. The organization's mission was:

To provide the necessary skills and supports so that each individual may lead a satisfactory and successful life in the setting of his or her choice with maximum use of community resources.

Dennis recounted that early in the organization's existence they were struggling with treating folks who had severe illnesses in a group—a milieu intervention—and that this was not achieving their mission. Dennis became so committed to equipping staff with the skills they needed to accomplish the mission that he contracted with an outside organization to teach his staff those practitioner skills that help people make positive changes in their lives. To evidence his commitment to this direction, Dennis took the training along with his staff, and then learned how to be a trainer himself. At the time of his interview, three full-time trainers had been hired to deliver what he calls the "rehabilitation teaching approach." Dennis spoke confidently, "we believe we now have the capacity to take any innovation and train people in it." The fabric of the Alternatives Unlimited program was psychiatric rehabilitation, and the training technology helped Dennis and his staff provide effective rehabilitation services. Training necessitated a rewriting of job descriptions and associated performance criteria. They had to do away with some tasks that were not relevant and redefine others. The more mundane, but important tasks of cooking and cleaning in the residences remained necessary, but they became tasks that were now integrated into the residents' rehabilitation goals. Dennis observed:

We integrated and re-prioritized many things into training opportunities for both staff and service recipients. Staff meetings became study groups and house meetings included time for skill teaching.

> Strong leadership is needed to overcome the natural reluctance that many mental health organizations exhibit to being trained in a human technology.

Strong leadership is needed to overcome the natural reluctance that many mental health organizations exhibit to being trained in a human technology. As Kathryn Power suggested previously in this chapter, mental health staff and their teachers seem much more comfortable in the world of theory and concepts, than in the world of technology. For some, the very word technology seems an anathema to their humanistic orientation. They do not appreciate the interpersonal skills components of the technology that are, at its very core, ensuring that the technology is in fact humanistic. In many ways, this discomfort is similar to the way medical educators refuse to teach the human aspects of medical practice with the same verve and expertise as they do medical coursework. As a result, the human relationship (bedside manner) often is missing from health care delivery and often is noted in the confusion and complaints that service users express.

Cheryl Gagne of Boston, Massachusetts, who had been trained in human technology as part of her doctoral program in psychiatric rehabilitation at Boston University, understood staff's anxiety about learning new skills, and particularly the coaching and feedback that are a part of the skill learning process.

> Principle 5 is a principle we are guided by, but we recognize that we sometimes fall short in implementing it. Our service program recognizes the need for skill development in our staff and that we all need opportunities to learn, practice, and get feedback on our skill performance. We have some structures in place that help us with this principle, but we are in need of more. We have had staff training days that not only teach knowledge but also skills. We offer individual supervision and support for the performance of skills. Some staff love this and are eager to get feedback, while others tend to avoid opportunities for observation and feedback.

Cheryl continued on about the critical need for staff to learn and receive feedback on their teaching skills, as most of her staff functioned in a teaching role.

> All staff receive feedback on their teaching performance from program participants. The feedback form we use lists some of the critical skills of teaching, and there is space for comments about the staff person's general overall performance in his or her role. This feedback is reviewed with the staff person and the need for skill development may be discussed in regular supervision meetings. It's been an ongoing struggle to create a culture in which every staff person feels secure enough in his or her job and role to

allow for an ongoing free exchange of feedback. We are able to give positive feedback on specific skills in meetings, but it's less common for someone to acknowledge his or her need for skill development in a public forum. We continue to work hard on this principle with the recognition that for some staff, any suggestion that there is room for improvement, feels like a threat.

Other mental health staff and organizations resist the adoption of a human technology because they simply do not value human technology. The anti-technology forces believe that if their organization's values are appropriate and if they offer some helping procedures, then they will be able to achieve consumer outcomes. Although this sometimes may be true, the question is, can these practitioners and organizations be even more helpful if they are equipped with a focus on the effective use of human technology? Can the various outcomes of people with serious mental conditions be further improved? Using a medical analogy again, can we progress beyond the 19th century doctor whose values seemed to be in the right place but whose medical knowledge was extremely limited, to a knowledgeable 21st century practitioner, whose values are still in the right place and who is educated in a human technology that enables the practitioner to interact more skillfully?

> Using a medical analogy... can we progress beyond the 19th century doctor whose values seemed to be in the right place but whose medical knowledge was extremely limited, to a knowledgeable 21st century practitioner, whose values are still in the right place and who is educated in a human technology that enables the practitioner to interact more skillfully?

Estelle Douglas, the director of psychiatric rehabilitation at Hillside Hospital when she was interviewed, spoke about this resistance to the rigorous training in human technology that she introduced. "The resistance has to do with staff giving up some of their professional practice methods," Estelle believed. However, this resistance lessened as the training progressed. Estelle noted:

> The resistance was abated as they began to see how their competence was being enhanced. The whole issue of burnout I think comes strictly because you don't have good methods to work with the service users. As the training modules were rolled out, they became more receptive to the training.

However, the training team had to be "indefatigable" in working with the initial resistance and cynicism. As a leader, Estelle had to be strong in her commitment to the importance of her staff becoming expert in a technology rather than just a theory.

With respect to our other major example of human technology focused on in this chapter, i.e., the implementation of the technology of seclusion/restraint reduction, we have presented in previous chapters about seclusion/restraint reduction initiatives described by Gene Johnson and Charley Curie. They provided these seclusion/restraint reduction examples as illustrations for other principles, but these same leadership examples also speak to the importance of training staff in a human technology.

As the president/CEO of META Services Gene Johnson used the example in chapter 1 of how his leadership in seclusion/restraint reduction was brought about by the necessity to get the agency's practices aligned with the agency's transformed vision. The seclusion/restraint reduction initiative incorporated most all the ingredients of a human technology training effort: training in skills and related knowledge; revised and compatible policies; tracking and monitoring behavior; supervision and celebrations of success.

During Charley Curie's interview he reflected how, when he was Pennsylvania commissioner, that state's seclusion/reduction initiative was an excellent example of principle 2, centralizing by mission and decentralizing by operations. However, it was also a telling example of a human technology making a difference. As part of this seclusion/restraint implementation, among other things, Pennsylvania's state hospitals:

> ...changed the way we trained staff; discovered different kinds of de-escalation strategies; reinforced the view that the use of S/R was a treatment failure and not a treatment intervention; monitored progress; and rewarded staff.

One of us (KH) has been instrumental in implementing the technology of seclusion/restraint reduction from the very get go. Kevin recounted how that in 1999, while she was the assistant hospital administrator, the CEO of Atlantic Shores (now GEO Care, Inc.)/South Florida State Hospital attended the annual State Hospital Superintendent's Conference, hosted by the National Association of State Mental Health Program Directors, in Washington, DC. After hearing a presentation by Laura Prescott, a woman in recovery and president of Sister Witness, Inc., Sal Barbara, the CEO, came back to his facility with a goal to eliminate the use of seclusion and restraint. Sal basically gave this challenge to his leadership team, Bob Quam, COO, Valerie Devereaux, DON, and Kevin Huckshorn, assistant hospital administrator. Kevin remembered the work on changing the cultures of care and staff practices.

> We had no template on how to reduce the use of seclusion and restraint back then. There was little in the literature and we had to figure it out as we went along. I worked closely with our consumer staff, Gayle Bluebird and Tom Lane, as it seemed to me that finding out why conflicts were occurring on units was the first step. And they became detectives in trying to understand these institutional processes and the hospital practices that were causing conflict. Valerie also worked long hours with her nursing staff on understanding how poorly handled staff to resident conflict could lead to using seclusion and restraint.

> Bob, Valerie, and I knew right from the start that staff behaviors and practices were key to being successful in this initiative. As we learned about institutional rules that were causing conflict, such as restrictions to rooms, waiting in lines, the lack of active treatment programs, overcrowding, lack of access to telephones or personal belongings, noise, confrontational language, and specific behaviors by some staff; we began to understand what had to change. We included nursing staff representatives in this work, and Valerie designed annual reviews that we all participated in—a nursing competency process titled "demonstration: return demonstration" of best practices related to de-escalation and negotiation skills. We provided new knowledge and attitudes about the use of seclusion and restraint and why these practices were no longer believed to be either effective or helpful in the long run. But we did not stop there. Unit nurse managers provid-

Though we were unsure at the beginning about how staff would receive these messages, that same staff rose to the occasion, changed their practices, and were successful in reducing the use of seclusion and restraint by over 95% from baseline in 1998.

ed role modeling behaviors and daily supervision to other nursing staff and reported on this work almost daily at the executive management group meetings. Rigorous analyses of every event that resulted in the use of seclusion, restraint, or injury were undertaken. And, though we were unsure at the beginning about how staff would receive these messages, that same staff rose to the occasion, changed their practices, and were successful in reducing the use of seclusion and restraint by over 95% from baseline in 1998.

As illustrated by the previous S/R reduction example, the organizational culture has to be supportive of human technology if the organization's training programs are to succeed. Culture has a strong influence on the adoption of any technology. Initial acceptance of a technology is not necessarily due to the worth of the technology itself, but rather to the readiness of the culture to accept it.

> Culture has a strong influence on the adoption of any technology. Initial acceptance of a technology is not due necessarily to the worth of the technology itself, but rather to the readiness of the culture to accept it.

The leadership, including senior and middle management staff, need to understand that part of their job tasks are to attend to the culture in a way that the training in human technology "takes." All of the previous examples of the implementation of seclusion/restraint technology at settings in Arizona, Pennsylvania, and Florida are great illustrations of how the organizational culture needs to be prepared and typically changed in order for the new technology actually to be used. It does not take much work to acculturate newly hired staff. It does take some expertise to prepare the culture so that already employed staff will be accepting of the new technology. But this work can and must be done.

Changes in staff behavior do not happen easily, and definitely not without the leader's constant attention to the importance of the new technology. Bob Quam and his executive team came up with leadership practices that helped to cement the training of staff in reducing the use of seclusion and restraint at Atlantic Shores (now GEO Care, Inc.)/South Florida State Hospital. First, Bob started making daily rounds on all of the eight residential units and the treatment mall. He would wander through these units, often talking to service users about their experiences, recognizing staff by name, and thanking them. This kind of work took a lot of time out of his day, but Bob, knew early on that staff needed to see their leaders and would benefit from this kind of daily communications. In addition, the South Florida State Hospital executive staff came up with many ideas on how to reward staff for best practices, including being identified at town hall meetings, being provided with funds for unit pizza parties, and being recognized through individual certificates that went into personnel files.

The leaders of an organization must develop a training mindset in their organizations that reinforces the importance of employees learning new skills and developing the accompanying attitudes necessary to use these skills, rather than just learning facts and concepts. Thus, training success cannot simply be measured by indices of staff involvement and satisfaction. The training outcome focus must be, primarily, on staff behavior change. Staff behavior will change as a function of gaining new skills, new knowledge, new attitudes, and ongoing supervision related to these changes. Without training in human technology, the organization's training function will continue to be perceived as not relevant to the vision and mission of the organization. Each of the leaders highlighted in this chapter made sure technology training aimed at their human capital was embedded in their organization.

> Staff behavior will change as a function of gaining new skills, new knowledge, new attitudes, and ongoing supervision related to these changes.

Besides the technology of psychiatric rehabilitation and seclusion/restraint reduction used as examples in this chapter, some leaders spoke about other issues related to implementing human technologies. Jim Reinhard from Virginia affirmed that the importance of human technology extended throughout the organization, including leadership skills for everyone in the organization.

> It's all about leadership. Everyone, no matter where they are in the organization, has to have a component of leadership in their skill set. The organization is not just made up of leaders, supervisors, and folks with technical skills. You look at all staff as a sort of

circle, with these three fundamental competencies important for every individual (leadership skills, management skills, and technical skills).

To repeat: training must be linked to the corporate mission. Too often an organization's training programs consist of introducing trendy new concepts to staff for their entertainment value. Over the short term, staff often are satisfied that they learned some interesting new concepts from an exciting speaker. Yet, if this is what constitutes the organization's staff training program, is it any wonder that the training function is often the first to go during times of organizational budget cutting. Years ago, one of us (WA) remembers looking at a training plan for a particular state and thinking how disjointed, uncoordinated, and irrelevant to the mission it was. The leader's state training director had presentations exposing the staff to all the latest concepts and fads, like assertiveness training and EST training; clearly this popular training was not very reflective of the new direction of the state department of mental health, which at that time was emphasizing community integration.

> Training must be linked to the corporate mission.

Thomas Kirk from Connecticut had concerns about how well the state's training plan was linked to the organization's vision, mission, and priorities.

> There are thousands and thousands of dollars in time that we commit for training. But is the training in accord with the focused priorities we have identified? Co-occurring disorders were the major focus for this year. If we had done this better, three or four years ago, we'd be further along; we did it in too much of a shotgun kind of approach. We just thought that exposing staff to knowledge, in and of itself, was going to produce the change that we wanted, but it didn't.

Thomas believed the state's approach to training in cultural competency was a much better example.

> I signed a contract with a group out of Temple University who are specialists in this and we created an office of multicultural affairs. I selected one of their folks and made him the director. We infused

significant dollars to expose staff to knowledge related to cultural competence. We came up with a format that included extensive, months long training, and then staff took what they learned, in terms of a cultural competence approach and brought this approach back to the organization that they worked in, whether it was state operated or private, nonprofit. This training worked by exposing staff to knowledge, giving them practical experience in training, and then having them apply that knowledge under supervision. So now, for example, for every agency that we have under contract, there is language in their contract that requires attention to cultural competence. They must produce a cultural competence plan for their agency as part of the submission or for funding.

> This training worked by exposing staff to knowledge, giving them practical experience in training, and then having them apply that knowledge under supervision.

Similarly, Tony Zipple revised the policies and procedures underlying the training program at Thresholds in order to make it more mission compatible.

All new employee training was revised to reflect our commitment to recovery and Evidence-Based Practices (EBPs). We also changed our ongoing training to incorporate much more recovery and the use of EBPs, and used more consumer trainers, etc. To support this, we moved our training operations from human resources to our research department because research was one of the key drivers for our work at recovery and implementing EBPs. The use of training has been a key for us in evolving the culture and values of Thresholds. It gives us a lot of opportunity to talk about what is important. The very act of publishing a catalogue of training offerings, that says "Recovery and EBPs," helps staff to see what is important.

When she was interviewed, Lori Ashcraft was the executive director of the META Recovery Education Center (where Gene Johnson was the CEO). Lori is also a person in recovery from mental illness. Similar to Tony Zipple, she emphasized the importance of making sure that the new staff orientation and training plan reinforced and was connected to the vision and mission of META through various policies and procedures. Lori stated:

> When we first opened the Recovery Education Center (REC) at META, we hired mostly a peer workforce. Eventually we hired an entire peer workforce, but in the beginning, we became aware of a huge gap between existing policies and procedures and the new vision that was emerging as we added peers to our workforce in the REC. The existing policies and procedures required that our peer staff fit into an old paradigm that would have seriously limited the roles and responsibilities of peers and would not have allowed them to function in new roles and responsibilities and be all that they could be. At the same time, we needed to have some guidelines or agreements that we could all live by as we worked and learned together.
>
> I shared my concerns with our quality management director, who reluctantly agreed to let us come up with a new way, with the understanding that we would still fall under the organization's policy and procedure umbrella. However, we would translate those requirements into our own guiding principles in language that made sense to us and that reflected recovery principles. I didn't just do this work myself; I knew that for new guidelines to work for peer staff that they would need to be involved in their development. I waited until a circumstance developed for which we needed new guidelines, and then wrote up an invitation, in the form of a friendly letter, to all the staff to send suggestions. Others were invited to write policy letters too. After several months of doing this, we finally got to a point to where no more letters were being written. We took this as a sign that we had completed our policy and procedure manual for the time being. I then organized the letters into sections and gave everyone a copy. When we hire new staff, they get a copy of the policy letters to keep and to read so they know and understand the culture and agreements we've made for working together.

Leadership can ensure that not only the training, but also the ongoing supervision, are both linked to the organization's mission.

Leadership can ensure that not only the training, but also the ongoing supervision, are both linked to the organization's mission. Cheryl Gagne from Boston, whose earlier comments in this chapter pointed to the value that a human technology plays in her organization's culture, commented also on the importance of mission-related supervision. Cheryl recommended that during staff supervision, the supervisor models the very skills that supervisees are expected to use with the people they are trying to help. Cheryl further amplified this point.

> We treat each other with the same rehabilitation framework during supervision when talking about problems in the workplace. Rather than label a worker as a problem, we use rehabilitation technology to assist them to first articulate a professional goal (often by exploring problems with lack of success or satisfaction on the job) and then brainstorm the skills, supports, and opportunities the worker may use to reach his/her goal. By applying the mission and technology to supervision, we assist workers to get a true "lived experience" of the mission and technology.

In summary, if only training was designed to help people "work smarter," that is, to relate fully to one another, to teach better, and to possess certain human technologies designed to address certain high priority concerns (such as the unnecessary prevalence of conflict and violence), training then might be perceived as the most important part of an organization, even during resource cutbacks. Indeed, it is at times like these that staff who have been trained in elements of a human technology realize that their job security is reinforced because, with these skills, they know they are more useful to their organization, more credible to their clients, and more marketable to other organizations.

If only training was designed to help people "work smarter,"...to relate fully to one another, to teach better, and to possess certain human technologies designed to address certain high priority concerns (such as the unnecessary prevalence of conflict and violence); training then might be perceived as the most important part of an organization, even during resource cutbacks.

The bottom line is that incorporating human technology into an organization is not a simple process. Leaders need to appreciate the contributions of a human technology to consumer outcome, the effort it takes on the part of employees to master the technology, the inherent resistance to technology, and the need to provide the necessary organizational supports. Without strong leadership the employees will do their important work with service users based on what they have learned through trial and error, and their own attempts to translate facts and concepts into appropriate actions. Principled leaders know there is a better way.

Leaders need to appreciate the contributions of a human technology to consumer outcome, the effort it takes on the part of employees to master the technology, the inherent resistance to technology, and the need to provide the necessary organizational supports.

CHAPTER/PRINCIPLE 6

Leaders relate constructively to employees.

- The leader publicly recognizes staff contributions to the organization.

- The leader listens and expresses interest in what all levels of employees are doing.

- The leader engenders trust in the staff.

- The leader demonstrates understanding of the staff's perspectives.

- The leader models interpersonal relationships that are characterized by dignity and respect.

- The leader "thinks out loud" with staff.

- The leader knows that "front end" listening yields better outcomes.

- The leader coaches staff by first getting their perspectives before giving the leader's perspective.

Leaders relate constructively to employees.

Good followers lead their leaders—good leaders listen to their followers so they can.

—*William A. Anthony*

General Dwight D. Eisenhower used a simple device to illustrate the art of leading people. He used an ordinary piece of string to demonstrate how it could easily be pulled in any direction. "Try and push it though," he cautioned, "and it won't go anywhere. It's just that way when it comes to people." Most leaders who were interviewed for this text did not push their followers. Like Eisenhower's analogy, they tried to pull together with their followers, and realized that in order to pull together they needed a positive relationship with their staff.

Leaders interviewed for *Principled Leadership* regularly used the pronouns "we" in describing their organization's achievements. As a result, they shared the credit for whatever accomplishments they made. When one of us (WA) walked around Florida State Hospital with the hospital director, Bob Williams, he often stopped people in the hospital to introduce me to them. The introduction typically started like this: "Bill, I want you to meet so and so. She was the one who made a difference in such and such." Bob Williams was making the point that he had observed what they did and was taking another opportunity to publicly thank them for it. He could not have made this point if he had not personally known their story.

I (WA) had a similar experience when I toured Estelle Douglas' program at Hillside Hospital in New York City. When Estelle Douglas and I passed someone in the hall, she paused to introduce them to me. It was never a simple introduction. Estelle Douglas always included some story about how this person had been influential in bringing about change to the organization.

In many different ways leaders celebrate and recognize staff's accomplishments about which they have heard. A personal thank you in front of their peers, a public award ceremony, a formal certificate rewarding best practice, a week of free lunches, a public acknowledgment in a meeting, or a note to one's supervisor, etc.—all are a part of a leader's repertoire for building a positive relationship with their staff. Just like the concept of power, leaders know that when they give credit, they ultimately get credit; and part of that "credit" is a positive relationship with their staff. Raul Almazar of Illinois had to figure out how to recognize his staff:

> Just like the concept of power, leaders know that when they give credit they ultimately get credit; and part of that "credit" is a positive relationship with their staff.

> I think one of the most successful things that we've done is to figure out how to reward and honor staff in this hospital. We never had resources for any of that kind of thing. But I kept saying that we can't get a sense of community with staff unless we create time with them and can celebrate their successes. We ended up with a staff appreciation committee and basically I picked someone who had a lot of energy and I said, "go pick your members and manage this project." These were all direct care staff. I told them, "You guys do what you need to do, raise the money." People were just waiting for this opportunity. And within three months these folks had $4,000. They went to the people at the hospital and said how much money can you give us? They actually just started asking for money for their projects. I think they were able to get $2,000 first, and the doctors were generous, you know doctors, doctors were like, "of course." They got the $2,000, and they decided to do lunch sales and bake sales and all of that and they were able, this past March, to host our first Winter Ball. Yes, a formal event for all staff, held outside in the hall; the other thing that's happened was that they put out posters of trying to reach the goal and specific families started calling, saying "we've been trying to figure out a way to thank staff for the work that

they do." So we started getting donations, "on behalf of my son, I thank you for everything."

Another way that leaders can demonstrate leadership, with respect to this principle, is to take the time to listen, express interest, and remember what staff have told them. Thomas Kirk, mental health commissioner from Connecticut, said that of the state employees he met, he tried to "understand who these folks are as people because it's those qualities that are most important, not their credentials."

As an example, he recounted an interaction he had with a front office staff person at a regional mental health center.

> People tend to come in repeatedly for services, and she knows the clients, consumers, the patients; some better than others. She will see that some days they're coming in, and they're really thrilled because of something. They talk about what they're really excited about, usually something that happened in their personal life. Then another day, she says, they come in, and they're totally down in the dumps; something's bothering them. She's developed a rapport with them so that they'll talk about these things. She emphasized that she was not a clinician but sometimes, "the best that I can say to the person is that I'll pray for them." That kind of relationship in many ways maybe expands the definition of "therapeutic relationship;" in many ways, it is as important to the people coming to us for care, for the fancy therapies and medication, etc. And I believe that these staff, and what they have to say, is so important so I have made sure that we recognize them for their contribution.

Leaders who make a point of listening to their staff, not only demonstrate that they wish to understand, but also that they are interested in the ideas and actions of their staff. When Pam Womack was interviewed, she was executive director of the Mental Health Cooperative, a case management agency in Nashville, Tennessee. At the time of the interview, the agency provided case management, clinic services, and crisis inter-

> Leaders who make a point of listening to their staff, not only demonstrate that they wish to understand, but also that they are interested in the ideas and actions of their staff.

vention services; 1,840 individuals used case management services and over 1,300 used psychiatric clinic services. The crisis intervention service, which was a mobile crisis service, served the entire county, whether they were case management clients or not. They had a 7.5 million budget with over 170 staff, including 70 case managers, 5 physicians, and 5 nurses. They had changed from fee-for-service to a capitated-rate under a private managed care model. Pam's interest in her staff started during the hiring process. Before a person could be hired, they were interviewed, went to a team meeting, and rode with a team in the community. Pam believed that her staff were their agency's most important commodity. "We don't have a program or a building we can point to." She referred to the staff as "our most precious asset." If staff made mistakes, Pam stated, "you don't punish, you try to remediate. If you treat staff with respect, they will treat consumers with respect."

Partly to engender trust in her staff, Pam allowed staff meetings to be held without supervisors present. Staff were encouraged to come up with suggestions, and they did, such as vacation time available up-front so staff did not have to wait to earn it over time. Furthermore, Pam also recognized what was going on outside the work life of her staff. For example, a supervisor told her a pet dog of one of the case managers had cancer and suggested Pam send her a card with a doggy treat in it, which Pam gladly did, and which was most appreciated.

> If a positive relationship exists between leader and follower, then differences of opinion can be just that—rather than also a battleground for personality conflicts.

It is hard for followers to be disagreeable with leaders who are praising them. This is not to say that followers will not have differences in opinion with leaders; it is to say that a positive relationship can prevent these differences from becoming disagreeable. If a positive relationship exists between leader and follower, then differences of opinion can be just that—rather than also a battleground for personality conflicts.

The interpersonal skills that are a critical part of the technology of staff in a mental health organization (see chapter 5) are also a necessary part of the leader's tools. Larry Miller from Arkansas used his training as a therapist and psychiatrist to help him relate constructively to his staff. He believed you need to develop a:

...respectful, compassionate relationship not only with patients, but with staff as well. I think that my dealing in a respectful manner with the staff showed them that we can deal with service users in the same way.

Interpersonally skilled leaders who pay attention to their staff, listen to them, and demonstrate an understanding of their staff's perspective, will find it easier to lead. Many would-be leaders think that the only way they can impress, as leaders, is to talk. But leaders have to listen also, and people listen with their ears not their mouths. Effective leaders will agree that they learn most with their mouths shut and their ears and eyes open. Sometimes leaders' open mouths have been known to automatically close their ears and eyes.

Susan Dempsey ensured that she would have the time to listen to her staff by setting a specific schedule for this communication to occur. When Susan was interviewed, she was the founder of Step Up On Second Street in Santa Monica, California, and its director for 13 years. Susan was also a family member and a long time member of NAMI. Susan indicated that she founded the agency because of the lack of appropriate settings for people like her son, who had a diagnosis of schizophrenia. Susan wanted to create a program that was part of the community and provided social, vocational, and educational interventions. During the first 13 years of her leadership, the agency's space grew from 7,000 square feet to 21,000 square feet; 36 apartment sites were found; the budget increased to 2.4 million with 30 full-time staff and 15 part-time staff, 20% of whom were in recovery from drug abuse and severe mental illnesses. Over 900 different people were served per year.

> Interpersonally skilled leaders who pay attention to their staff, listen to them, and demonstrate an understanding of their staff's perspective, will find it easier to lead.

Because much of Step Up On Second Street's interventions were provided off-site and in the community, Susan made a special effort to listen regularly to her staff. Susan knew that "front end" listening would translate into more effective agency practices. Susan instituted a meeting with all staff, everyday from 5:00 to 5:30 P.M., to discuss critical incidents and communicate significant events of the day. Susan believed this also kept the culture alive with staff who were dispersed during the day. In addition, Susan felt that the opportunity to communicate acted as a "stress reliever" by helping staff to avoid taking work problems home at the end of the day. Susan was cognizant of her staff's time, and made sure that the agency had few meetings other than this one. They did not meet "just to meet."

The basic, most obvious, and most often forgotten truth is that people talk to people who are listening and are interested in them! Over time, employees will stop talking to leaders who don't listen. This is not rocket science, although rocket scientists who wish to be leaders must also operate on this fundamental truth. Without

> The most dangerous behavior a leader can demonstrate is a lack of interest in what his or her staff are saying, or needing, to do their jobs well.

staff input, leaders will lack the different perspectives they need to hear in order to make informed choices about their organization. The most dangerous behavior a leader can demonstrate is a lack of interest in what his or her staff are saying, or needing, to do their jobs well. And this includes the direct care staff, in fact this could be the most important group to know.

Lori Ashcraft of META Services in Phoenix Arizona believed strongly in the power of the relationship between leaders and staff.

> I believe that the relationship with staff is the strongest management tool a leader has, and the more positive it is, the better the result will be for the employee, as well as the person being served and the company as a whole. I try to create relationships that encourage the employees to have ownership in what they are doing and to feel indispensable to having it produce a positive outcome. I sometimes refer to this as the "Colombo" style of management, where I am the supposed bumbling boss, who gets others to figure out what the best course of action would be, and I am then very grateful that we can move ahead in the best direction. And I must say that this is not insincere on my part. I find that those working closest to the problem often have the best answers, so my role is really to just ask the right questions in an effort to get them to figure out what to do. I have developed a coaching system that includes an employee evaluation process

that puts the employees in the driver's seat in determining their performance goals, etc. My job may be mostly to stretch them to higher levels, or to point out things that they may have over-looked. Yes, the same form can be used for persons receiving serv-ices to develop a treatment plan. I hope to see the day when staff and people receiving services work together, using the same form, to discuss how they could support each other in developing the best plans, whether they are employees or people served. This is a tremendously effective way to level the playing field between staff and people being served.

Lori went on to point out that leadership needed to express inter-est and understanding to all staff, no matter what their level in the organization.

When we first started adding peer employees to our workforce, we found ourselves very invested in them being successful. We bent over backwards to help them learn their jobs, be responsible employees, keep their word, etc. If they didn't do well, we invest-ed more effort and more time and support into helping them suc-ceed. Usually they did. As our other staff watched this process, they developed some resentment. "What about us? We've been here for a long time, doing our best, and we never got this kind of support and attention form you." This was a big "heads up" for us, and we realized that our whole organizational culture needed to change. We needed to treat all of our staff with the same level of investment that we were showing the peer employees. I can't think of the specific instance where we became aware that we were not treating all staff equally. We just became aware of this inequity, acknowledged it, and set out to change our approach. We realized that we all needed to recover, not just the people we served.

Carkhuff and Berenson (1976) captured the interpersonal rela-tionship between leader and staff in the phrase, "get-give-merge-go," meaning leaders must first listen to someone else's perspec-tive, then give their perspective, then combine the two perspectives as needed, and then make the decision as to the appropriate action. In order for this get-give-merge-go process to work effectively, the leader must be interpersonally skilled.

Without using the phrase, get-give-merge-go, Larry Miller essentially described this process with the following example. As Larry Miller put it:

> If you ask staff for information or input, that's all well and good. But if you don't do something with it, at least sort of distilling it, summarizing it, giving it back to check if you are right—"this is what I heard, am I correct in the summary"—then people lose faith. I also believe in looking at the quick-fix kind of things you can do that demonstrate that you've heard and are interested in what they had to say. If you wait for the longer term outcomes, staff get frustrated or disappointed sometimes, and they will say, "I've heard this story before, so why is this different this time? What are you doing differently that I should buy into this? Why should I trust you?" It really has to do with the relationships you develop with your employees, in wanting and respecting their feedback, and in providing your own feedback to them.

By modeling what is meant by collaborative relationships, the leader can show staff the difference between coaching and ordering.

One of the tasks of leaders is to "coach" their organization, not with respect to the technical skills of their staff, but rather to coach people around the vision. Leaders must get their staff to work cooperatively towards the vision. By modeling what is meant by collaborative relationships, the leader can show staff the difference between coaching and ordering. Coaching is based on the concept of get-give-merge-go, and is grounded in the interpersonal skills of the leader.

When Dennis Rice of Alternatives Unlimited was interviewed, he knew full well the value of communicating like a coach. Like most of the leaders' comments in this chapter, his hypothesis was that the leaders' effective communication with their staff also improved the staff's relationship with the people they were serving.

> We believe that the quality of an organization is reflected in the importance it places in all its members, and that includes staff.

Similar to our mission for our service recipients, staff need to be successful and satisfied in their work environment. Communication is one vehicle to ensure this.

Dennis opined that you cannot communicate enough, and that coaching people around various issues is a critical part of this communication. "The leader communicates, communicates, communicates....You can't communicate enough." Dennis admitted that this extraordinary focus on communication took a great deal of effort. "The patience one has to have to communicate vision, values, and mission is a full-time job, even though a leader has many other things to do." Dennis noted that the leader often is talking big picture, and the worker is into the details of their day-to-day functioning. He believed that it was up to the leader to listen to the staff and try and make that link from one to the other.

> Employees who believe that their leader tries to listen and understand their perspective are almost by definition more motivated.

Much has been made over the concept of "management by wandering around." Leaders also have embraced this concept as a means to stay in touch with their staff. While the concept might make sense, the implementation of it is fraught with danger if the leader is not skilled interpersonally. Who wants to be around, much less be touched, by leaders who don't listen or understand? It is not the "wandering around" that makes the difference. It is in great part a function of the relationship skills of the leader who does the wandering around.

One of the major tasks of leadership is to mobilize or "motivate" employees toward the shared organizational vision and mission. Extrinsic rewards, such as salary, office size, and other perks are typical ways of motivating staff. Leaders in the public sector, however, also must focus on intrinsic rewards to mobilize people towards the organization's vision. Employees who believe that their leader tries to listen and understand their perspective are almost by definition more motivated. People simply work harder and smarter for people who demonstrate their caring for them. Again, it's not rocket science, but human science.

Leaders who relate constructively to their employees engender trust. In order for leaders to be most effective, they must be trusted by their staff to do what is right for the organization. To get staff to trust them, leaders must model trust. They must be willing to take a risk when it comes to trusting their employees. Leaders cannot force people to trust them, but leaders who are interpersonally skilled and demonstrate their trust in their followers will be rewarded by trusting employees. Len Stein's pathfinding innovation, in treating folks with severe mental illnesses in the community rather than in the hospital, could not have been accomplished without building mutual trust between staff and the leadership.

> Leaders who relate constructively to their employees engender trust.

Elizabeth Childs of Massachusetts talked about the need for trust between leaders and staff so that leaders could receive honest feedback from their own staff.

> The obstacles for leaders in getting good feedback was an important topic in a message that someone told me when I first took this job and, boy, did this become true really quickly. My messenger said, "as soon as you're in the position, everyone will stop telling you the truth, and instead tell you what they think you want to hear. I believe you don't want that. You want people around you who will brutally honest with you." That important message made me aware, so now I measure my senior leaders on their honesty. When I do their performance reviews, I talk to them about how much information they have brought to me, about issues and concerns. And also about how proactive they have been.

An example of this honest type of feedback was provided by Elizabeth.

> I expect managers to come forward with constructive criticism, and thankfully, I have managers who will say, "I observed you in that event the other night, and I think there's something here that might help you do that more effectively next time around." One manager recently told me that she felt that when I made a joke while I was running a statewide forum, that my laughing dimin-

ished my presence in the room. I think that takes a lot of guts for a manager to say that to you. It was someone whom I trust a great deal, and she had brought this to me because she thought it would make me really think about this the next time. As a result, I am more conscious of these kinds of things now. Effective leaders surround themselves with people who will be honest with them and their other staff. This requires a certain trust.

Bennis and Nanus (1985) have defined trust as the emotional glue that binds followers and leaders together. As trust accumulates, leaders are seen as more legitimate. Bennis and Nanus believe that trust is encouraged when leaders' vision is clear and their behavior is consistent with the vision. As a result, leaders are seen as reliable and persistent. Their relentless dedication helps to engage the trust in their followers. Leaders who "stay the course" with respect to the importance of the leader/staff relationship, have employees who trust them. The trust is personal. It does not mean that leaders will never change, because indeed they will. What it does mean is that their interpersonal skills and fundamental way of relating to their staff will not change—even while their ideas change.

> As trust accumulates, leaders are seen as more legitimate.

In a trusting, human relationship between leaders and followers, leaders also can disclose personal information about themselves. Followers appreciate the trust leaders show to them when they self-disclose. Followers often remember hearing the leader's self-disclosure more than the leaders remember self-disclosing. This difference in recall of leader self-disclosure is due to the fact that leadership self-disclosure, while perhaps not that big a deal for the leader, often has a powerful, positive impact on followers. Followers naturally wish to know more about their leaders. Leaders who accommodate this wish are in actuality helping to develop their ability to lead.

As was suggested in chapter 1, leaders usually do not develop the organization's vision in isolation. They may choose the initial vision, but rarely do they create the final vision all by themselves. Thus, the leader must be an excellent listener, skilled not just in answering, but in asking questions and then listening to the answers. When Mike Hogan was director of the Ohio mental health system, he reflected on the importance of the relationship between himself and his staff. Mike said one of the biggest challenges was described by principle 6.

> We have had to focus on issues related to what's involved in being a good family? Questions were asked of each other, such as: "Am I getting support from you on this, or, are we really together on this?" When we were clear about the big picture, and when we were clear about our relationships with one another, we were able to do things very efficiently.

> When we were clear about the big picture and when we were clear about our relationships with one another, we were able to do things very efficiently.

Mike felt that if people don't feel like communication between them is happening, "then a very small thing can become a big problem." Mike's leadership style was an interpersonal style into which he believed he has grown. Earlier in his career, he indicated that he would get frustrated when talking about something at length before doing something about it. He described himself as an introvert and a conceptual thinker. When he was a deputy commissioner in Connecticut, he learned that conversations about things that didn't seem important at the time, were important in developing relationships, and as he put it, "positioned us better to follow through on decisions after they had been made. Collaboration with staff is very powerful." He reasoned that this collaborative style could coexist with his conceptual style, and that each had added value.

Elizabeth Childs of Massachusetts commented on the importance of front-end listening, which she said is especially important for instances when staff disagree with your decision.

> Even people who disagree with your decision can appreciate that you took their point of view into consideration. I think that this is possibly the only way that staff can understand how helpful their contribution was, whatever the final decisions. And it may help some staff to get behind whatever decision you did make. I think that works much better than saying "this is the decision; everybody get behind it or get out of here."

Followers who have leaders who relate constructively to them experience a feeling of being pulled along, together, with the leader. In contrast, in a poor leader/follower relationship, leaders give followers the experience of being pushed, sometimes away, sometimes back, but rarely forward. Expert leaders, by virtue of their relationship with their staff, give followers a sense of community. Leadership is not competitive but collaborative. Leaders who only wish to impress their followers clearly don't wish to learn from their followers. It is the relationship between leaders and followers that allows reciprocity between leaders and followers. The leaders' interpersonal skills are as critical as their conceptual skills in gathering the information they need to be constantly improving their organization. That information is often residing in their followers' heads. The way for the leader to access that information most effectively is often through their followers' hearts as well as their heads.

> The leaders' interpersonal skills are as critical as their conceptual skills in gathering the information they need to be constantly improving their organization.

Leaders access and use information to make change a constant ingredient of their organization.

- The leader uses information to frame problems in new and unique ways.

- The leader sees information as the organization's capital.

- The leader uses information to create new meaning for the organization.

- The leader uses information to anticipate the future.

- The leader looks for opportunities to "stay in touch" with the environment.

- The leader thrives on change.

- The leader initiates change rather than manages change.

- The leader recognizes that maintaining the status quo is actually moving the organization backwards.

- The leader recognizes that when you are doing things well, it is time to make them better.

- The leader discriminates when consensus is and is not necessary in order for change to occur.

- The leader can still ensure involvement and participation without always achieving consensus prior to a change.

- The leader recognizes that a clear vision and values facilitate consensus to change.

- The leader knows that while planning for change is good, allegiance to plans may not always be appropriate.

- The leader realizes that changing information can change carefully constructed plans.

Leaders access and use information to make change a constant ingredient of their organization.

Embracing change is a constant challenge for leaders.

—*William A. Anthony*

Leaders covet change. Not in the negative sense of the word "covet," but in the positive sense, that is, leaders eagerly desire change because they know that change brings constant opportunities. It makes no difference whether their organization is performing well or poorly. Effective leaders realize that constant change is a necessity.

As described by Linda Rosenberg, who was interviewed at the time she was the director of the National Council of Community Behavioral Healthcare:

> I am very conscious of principle 7. I think it is vitally important. Nothing stays the same. If you stay the same, you will go backwards. It's one of the problems about strategic plans. There are moments in time you really need a nimble organization that can take advantage of opportunities as they come along, and I think the leader has to be able to have a vision of how those pieces could fit together. So if there's a crisis, how do you make the crisis part of moving your agenda? Sometimes a crisis can help you move your agenda because people are less defensive and you need to take those opportunities. I think this notion of change as a constant is a fact of life. You have to show the people in your organization that it's always going to be that way and that we look at it as an opportunity to do better work.

Importantly, effective change is often based, in part, on the organization's capital. As explained by Carkhuff and Berenson (2000b), organizational capital is not just physical resources, such as a building, land, and money. It is also the information that the organization possesses. Capital is simply another word for what's most important. And one of the most important parts of an organization is that information they have now and what they can get.

As you will read about later in this chapter, one of Charley Curie's goals at SAMSHA was to change the way people with co-occurring disorders were assessed and treated. In order to make the needed policy decisions, Charley knew that part of his agency's capital was accurate information on this topic.

> When I came aboard, the debate was a data debate. The mental health people were saying 50% or more people in service had a co-occurring substance abuse disorder, or a co-occurring mental health disorder, and the health people were saying that it was less then 2%. We are able to do household surveys and other surveys and used the data to demonstrate that the range was realistically 20 to 25% of people had serious mental illness and addictive disorders. Then, we were able to make decisions.

When Richard Surles assumed the leadership in New York State, he found a discrepancy between what was said and what the data indicated.

> When I went to New York, everyone was saying that everything was about community-based services and aftercare. But when you looked at the resource allocations, 90% of the resources were allocated to the state hospitals. The data indicated that there was no match between people saying the politically correct thing and how resources were being allocated. I couldn't agree more with the importance of this principle about the need for information and the constancy of change.

Elizabeth Childs, in Massachusetts, also reinforced how information capital is critical to leadership.

> Everything that I think is critical about leadership has to be grounded in principles and values, but you cannot implement

decisions based on ideology and values alone. You have to have good, solid, accurate data and analysis. I think leaders get themselves into big trouble when they make decisions based on ideology alone. It's the place to start, but it's not the place to stop. I greatly value vision, values, and principles, but the next step is being very careful about the kind of information that you're listening to. I think we see some big mistakes that great leaders have made when they've only listened to one piece of information, and they haven't really had at their fingertips, all of the critical accurate data and information that they needed to make good decisions. It is the responsibility of your staff to get that to you and to make sure you see it. I think good leaders set a tone that this need for accurate and measurable data is an expectation, and I've done this with all my mangers. They are all clear on this expectation, and I expect managers to say to me "you're missing a key piece of information here, and this is what it is."

The previous quotes on information capital from Curie, Surles, and Childs reinforce the importance of data as a means to get at the facts; facts that may be contrary to what people want to hear or want to say; facts that often go unsaid. This data can help the leader get closer to reality; the vision cannot be pursued well without the vision's grounding in what the truth actually is. The principled leader must be diligent in searching the data for what is real. Often in mental health, we have deceived ourselves into believing what we want to hear rather than discovering our consumers' reality, uncomfortable as it might be.

Mental health leaders need to have information about consumers they are helping, about other people and organizations that are helping these same consumers, and about how their own organization's services are uniquely benefiting the people they serve. Without such information, the organization cannot effectively change or manage operations. Indeed, there will be low pressure on the organization to change if they still are operating on yester-

> Mental health leaders need to have information about consumers they are helping, about other people and organizations that are helping these same consumers, and about how their own organization's services are uniquely benefiting the people they serve.

day's information. When Terry Cline was in Oklahoma he said, "I talked constantly about the need to change." Throughout his tenure, directing mental health operations in numerous states, Richard Surles was uncompromising in his search for new and cutting edge information to bring about change.

So too was Thomas Kirk, the commissioner in Connecticut. Tongue in cheek, Thomas opined, "We have a lot of data, but we don't necessarily have a lot of information." He continued:

It is a joke around my group that they'll say, "if you've got to bring something to the commissioner, you know what he's going to say. He is going to say, show me data; show me whatever information or data you have that would somehow reinforce your point of view." There's a very, very, strong focus on data in Connecticut, on marrying the data with information and using that information to manage change.

An example of Connecticut's use of data was Thomas' description of how, during the budget process, they had to decide what services should receive a priority.

We looked at the effect of stable housing on folk's service cycles. We studied our data that say that persons who have access to stable housing have a higher rate of employment or involvement in educational activities, and diminished reliance on inpatient services. We learned from our data that safe and adequate housing increased the overall quality of care and that our investment in stable housing gave us a higher value. I use the equation that "value equals quality divided by cost."

Unfortunately, not all information collected is useful, and sometimes the purpose of collecting the information has disappeared. When Rupert Goetz arrived to be medical director at the Hawaii State Hospital, he found that information was abundant, but not used to improve the organization.

When I came three years ago, we had an enormous amount of information about an enormous number of things. When I scratched under the surface, that data was only part of the whole; wherever you looked, there were all these little databases. People were collecting information and preparing reports constantly; on some level, the organization was expert at developing information and generating reports. What the organization was extremely poor at was doing anything meaningful with that data. In other words, all the data just generated reports that people were constantly being expected to turn in. Staff knew they were going to be held accountable about producing it, and they thought of it as a constant set of fire drills that really didn't have much organizational meaning.

So I thought about how could we address this? We wound up making our performance improvement committee one of the core committees in the whole organizational committee structure. I took the prerogative as medical director and made myself chair of the committee. My goal was to make our data collection relevant to what is going on, clinically, on the units. So what we did then, as a performance improvement committee, was to teach the organization how to collect the important information. We are currently working on performance measures that track key issues, such as our rehabilitation and recovery outcomes and specific outcomes that are related to our forensic populations.

> What leaders need are data relevant to the mission and vision of the organization.

Rupert Goetz effectively illustrated the downside of data in his important contribution. Sometimes information is not lacking—it is simply overwhelming in its complexity and enormity. Leaders with a vision and mission, however, can cut through this data debacle more easily and begin to look for mission and vision compatible data. What leaders need are data relevant to the mission and vision of the organization. What leaders often get is everything else.

Effective leaders also cannot look at data with a blind eye; that is, without understanding what they are seeing. For instance, the National Association of State Mental Health Program Director's Research Institute tracks data on the use of seclusion and restraint events for the state public hospitals. In 2007, a review of this data showed an almost flat trend line, after significant decreases, starting in 2005. Many people became confused and discouraged about this lack of progress, especially since many facilities were reporting progress. However, Bob Glover and Noel Mazade started asking questions. And it became clear that because the Centers for Medicare and Medicaid had changed the definitions of what constituted restraint in 2003, hospitals now were counting many more events. It was obvious that this national trend line really did not reflect current practice, just a change in data collection procedures. It is important for leaders to "know enough" about the data they track to be able to make well-informed decisions about what these data really mean.

> It is important for leaders to "know enough" about the data they track to be able to make well-informed decisions about what these data really mean.

As the director of services at Boston University's Center for Psychiatric Rehabilitation, Dori Hutchinson knew that her organization had to continue to change, and that the status quo was not acceptable, no matter how painful change might be to staff. Dori made sure that she had the information she needed to help her organization change by staying in touch with the people served as well as the research literature.

In both my professional and personal life, I am very committed to the idea that change is a constant in life, not the exception. Thus I believe that responsiveness to change is critical to providing services that will help someone to lead a life with meaning and purpose. I operationalize this in multiple ways through my leadership of our services. We seek regular feedback from our participants through a monthly advisory board, and we encourage the participants to constructively criticize our practices, policies, and personal behaviors. And they do. And often, it is not easy to hear. But I believe that in every complaint, there is at least a grain of truth, if not the whole truth, and we actively try to respond to the issues that are brought to us by our participants. As a result, to be responsive, we often end up changing what we had planned to do. We start new services based on what people say they want and need, and what the research is suggesting mental health service delivery needs to "be" in order to meet our mission on a regular basis. I have learned two things about this practice. I must immediately and frequently communicate the reason for the change and identify the relevance of the change to our mission and values for both the participants and the staff. I must acknowledge that change is painful, even when it promises to bring better outcomes and more meaningful services. Often I have to work hard to persuade staff that they can endure the changes and that the previous plan was just that, a plan, not a blueprint. Perhaps resistance to change is human nature, but I have learned that resistance to change and a rigid approach are disempowering, disheartening, and deplete the hope of recovery. I now actively seek staff who can roll with the punches, who are not afraid of change, who are willing to struggle to change, and who are willing to support others while they try to change. This willingness to change is not only an environmental ingredient, but a personal ingredient, and an essential job requirement that I find critical to successful leadership.

> Willingness to change is not only an environmental ingredient, but a personal ingredient, and an essential job requirement that I find critical to successful leadership.

Besides seeking information on which to make needed changes, leaders must ensure that everyone can access information. "Everyone" includes consumers and their family members. Innovation and change builds on the premise that all important people in the organization have the latest information. Whether it is access to computer databases, conferences, organizational newsletters, etc., all parts of the organization need to be as informed as is possible. Judy Trysnicki, the president of Housing Options Made Easy (HOME), believed that change in her organization must be based on information and be constant. Consistent with her value of consumer input, she saw the information gleaned from the consumers of her organization's services to be her organization's capital, as important she said as new information from research or information about new government regulations. For example, she learned from people using HOME's services that access to services needed to be improved. As

> Besides seeking information on which to make needed changes, leaders must ensure that everyone can access information.

a result, HOME created satellite offices and an 800 number to make information easier to get.

One of the unique pressures of leadership is information pressure—caused either by an overwhelming amount of information and/or by the lack of useful information. Effective leaders become anxious if they can't get the accurate information they need. As leaders get information, the information itself impacts the leaders, resulting in the leaders' need for more information or for a different type of information. The quest for new information is continuous. And, as most leaders who understand the performance or quality improvement approach, this is a never-ending activity that requires prioritization way beyond a quarterly meeting where data are presented through dehumanized charts and accepted passively.

After Sandy Forquer left her position as deputy commissioner in New York State, she became head of the Colorado Health Network, which was run by Options, a private-for-profit managed care firm. She was interviewed during her time at the Colorado Health Network, where she implemented a "culture of measurement" throughout the many service programs that were under her leadership. Data were her organization's capital, and she used it constantly to make needed changes. Sandy tied the vision and the importance of measurement together. "You really cannot know where you are in terms of your vision if you are not measuring." One of many examples Sandy provided was her expectation to measure each hospital's readmission rate, which was then compared to all other hospitals in the network. A hospital that was performing significantly below average was prioritized for assistance.

> You really cannot know where you are in terms of your vision if you are not measuring.

> We went in and found out the specific causes of their underaverage performance and provided an educational intervention focused on their hospital discharge procedures. The next time we looked at readmission data, their performance had changed dramatically.

The distance between data-defined reality and the organization's shared vision is always present. A vision is always farther away than present day reality, or it isn't a vision! However, this space between vision and reality cannot obscure the facts. Rather, this vision/reality gap can translate into a motivational source of energy that is used creatively to shorten the distance between vision and reality.

Terry Cline mentioned how staying in touch with certain parts of the environment not only provided information, but also inspired him.

> You find yourself saying it's time for an afternoon or a day of site visits. I'm going to go out and have conversations with people who are actually touched by these services. I'm going to talk with people who are providing these services out in the field; the people I don't see every day. One result of the way we structure the administration and bureaucracy, and everything else that we do, is that sometimes we feel very removed from the people we are serving. And, for me, it takes one story from a consumer, just to put it in perspective. I remember visiting a program that was a couple of hours from here, and I walked into a clubhouse and they said, "Dr. Cline, come over here and talk to so and so." I can play these times back and that's my inspiration; hearing these individual stories of change, and just the perseverance of people who have had the odds stacked against them their entire lives and how they have persevered and prospered. They are in recovery and doing well and helping spread the message of recovery to their friends. I mean—how could that not inspire you? It's a reminder of why I do everything else, which is everything from asking for money for services to dealing with laws and legislation and rules and handling tons of paper work; that is the reason we do it.

Richard Surles strongly emphasized the leader's responsibility to stay in touch with all parts of the environment; not just the mental health environment.

> What's the context in which the organization lives? What are the key influences? What is it that people are articulating that are external to the organization that cause the problems with which they must deal? I think the role that I probably played the most in every place I've been, is my responsibility to understand the environment in which the organization's embedded and what peo-

ple's perceptions are regarding that organization. Part of the leader's responsibility is to really know who the external influences are and to then influence them. Mike Hogan is a great example of a leader with this ability.

> Part of the leader's responsibility is to really know who the external influences are and to then influence them.

If leadership does not consider the larger environment in which the organization functions, many new organizational initiatives will be doomed to failure. Little is gained, and much leadership credibility is lost, by advancing plans for which resources and supports simply do not exist. In the political vernacular, such initiatives are DOA, dead on arrival.

Steve Mayberg from California also emphasized that a leader must understand more than just the mental health system.

> We need to talk to people who do not access us and find out why. When you look at any kind of satisfaction studies or outcomes studies, these always are done with the people who are in our system and not the people who hate the system. I knew our system could never change unless we started talking to the people who hate the system to find out why.

Steve went on to name another group from which information was lacking in his system: the Native American community. He needed information on what they wanted, but also how to get that information.

> I scheduled a meeting with all tribal leaders and asked one of the leaders to give me a consultation on how to run a meeting. This tribal leader said their value system in terms of running meetings was antithetical to how bureaucracies run meetings. Because of this, I turned the meeting over to the Native American community. I invited them to my office and turned it over to them. The meeting started with a blessing, then the elders talked first, and I just listened and did not respond because it is not appropriate to interrupt. Listening to what the elders have to say is important.

One of the critical tests of leaders is to process the information they receive. It is in the processing of information that leaders develop entirely new responses to a particular organizational problem. When everyone has the same current, up-to-date information (and in this information age they should be able to get it), what is then most important is how the information is processed. Dennis Rice, the director of Alternatives Unlimited, in Whitinsville, Massachusetts was privy to the information that the model of traditional halfway houses for people with severe mental illnesses left much to be desired. Alternatives was one of the first agencies to change to a supported housing approach, and Dennis did so based on information he was generating from the people and staff who were living in the halfway houses. Alternatives collected information on what was occurring each hour in their housing program, and they found that less time was spent in crisis intervention than expected. This information helped them change to a new supported housing model that was less focused on hourly supervision. Dennis remarked:

> One of the critical tests of leaders is to process the information they receive. It is in the processing of information that leaders develop entirely new responses to a particular organizational problem.

> ...nonprofits are in business to change people or society—we are in the business of change—it's part of the culture. It's easy for us to change as we are not attached forever to certain models but to positive change.

As suggested by Terry (1993), leaders like Dennis Rice must use the information to frame issues correctly, that is, to answer the question, what is really going on? The ability of leaders to use information to see new possibilities and create new opportunities enables leaders to choose or modify their organization's vision, mission, goals, and activities—even though their options may be seen by others to be severely limited. Effective leaders seem to frame the problem differently than non-leaders. They access the same information but see different things. For example, when Len Stein saw the problem of hospital recidivism, he did not use the information that he possessed (and was possessed by most everyone else in the country) to

> The ability of leaders to use information to see new possibilities and create new opportunities enables leaders to choose or modify their organization's vision, mission, goals, and activities—even though their options may be seen by others to be severely limited.

frame the problem as how to improve the hospital system. Rather, he created a non-hospital alternative because he saw the problem as lack of support to live in the community rather than simply improving the capacity of the hospital.

Joe Parks used information to create new meaning for the organization and to initiate a change process within the organization. When Joe was interviewed, he was the medical director of comprehensive psychiatric services for the Missouri Department of Mental Health.

> One of the early tasks that we had to deal with was to improve the integration between the mental health division and the substance abuse division, at all levels, including the leadership. Both sides were feeling that the other was non-responsive; there was this general approach of telling consumers to go to the other service. You know, "he's not our patient, he's that other system's patient." Everybody was making a point of accentuating the differences. Whenever there was a dialogue, the dialogue would be about everything that was dissimilar about the two fields; everyone would get frustrated and conclude that the whole discussion was pretty pointless.
>
> So when I decided to take this on, I started going with the data, with using data to redefine people's perception of the environment they were in. The first thing we did was look for the overlap between the two divisions as they currently existed. Our acute hospitals were complaining that they were getting all the substance abusers. We ran some numbers and when we analyzed the data, only 25% of the bed days were being used for people who were there solely, or primarily, for a substance abuse disorder. Along with that we did a chart review of people who came in with sole or primary substance abuse disorders to see if they looked like inappropriate admissions. By and large, they were not inappropriate admissions, in that there was no better alternative service for them.

Joe reframed the issue of inappropriate admissions to one of inappropriate care. He laid out the expectations, and provided additional resources.

> We tended to their concerns of being overwhelmed, but made our expectations clear, provided training, provided staff with breathalyzers and urine test equipment so they could detect drugs, and improved the lab turnaround times. The hospitals also were terrified that if they got better at doing substance abuse treatment, they would get more people. We reframed that as saying that we're not asking you to take anybody new, we're just asking you to do better with the people you've been unsuccessful in avoiding anyway!

Next Joe used data to look at how folks were doing in the community and found that each division was doing a poor job of diagnosing people, who should be receiving services from the other division as well. Using the data as support, the department initiated a major change.

> And we used data to good effect. We actually changed our final vision as a result of that data. We decided about six years in that we were no longer going to focus on a "collaborative model" as the way to go. We were going to focus on an "integrated model" rather than trying to get agencies to pair up, which they could only do for short periods of time anyway, even when they intended to do more. We held out for the expectation that every mental health agency would be competent in treating substance abuse to the extent they found that a current condition of their patient population, and that a substance abuse agency would be competent in treating mental illness to the extent they found that present in their substance abuse patient population.

> We started out saying "we think the reason that you're having relapse in your substance abuse treatment population is because you're not addressing their mental illness needs, or we think the reason that you are having a lot of recidivism in your mental health population is because you're not addressing substance abuse. Half your people have both conditions, and you can't have good outcomes unless you get better at treating this other condition." We said repeatedly that we're not asking you to take anybody new. That caused them some relaxation among the providers, I believe.

Similarly, Elizabeth Childs described how her pursuit of information allowed her to reframe the problem of how to close a state hospital.

> We were faced with a significant budget cut, and the governor had publicly said he was closing a hospital. I said to my deputy, "We're going to go out there, and we're going to walk every inch of these buildings; we're going to talk to the patients, talk to the staff, and figure out what the right thing to do here is for the people we are serving. We're going to figure out what the right thing to do is, and then we're going to make that happen. It may not be what they want to hear, but that's what we're going to tell them." So we walked every inch of these facilities, a million square feet, crawling through corridors, tunnels, and everything trying to understand it. These buildings are not adequate, in any way, to provide recovery-oriented treatment. They're ancient; they're undignified; they're disrespectful. It's a sample of what the consumers talk about; they are not safe in my book and, God only knows, people seeking services deserve adequate treatment in inpatient settings, almost above all others due to acuity and cost.
>
> I remember driving home on the turnpike; I was so discouraged because the way this decision had been presented to us was that we would have to close one of them. Neither building was adequate to allow us to close one and put everybody in the other one, or even put some of the people in the other one. And I decided that we needed to close them both. We needed a new facility and that we could decrease our total number of beds. But the new beds would have to represent high quality care and effective treatment. This is when my senior team and I did a thorough analysis of our data, went through every utilization trend we could find in Massachusetts, measured our trends over a decade, and figured out how many people we had in the hospitals who could be served in the community with an infusion of dollars. We did a lot of work and compared our data with peer states. We developed a report, and I presented that to the Secretary of Health and Human Services for Massachusetts. I basically said this is the right thing to do. The right thing to do here is not to close a hospital and do nothing. If you want to close a hospital, you

ought to close both of them, build a new and smaller one, and put dollars in the community to support people who could live there.

Then I worked with the legislature; we had a legislative feasibility commission, so I had tremendous broad bipartisan legislative support. The consumers and NAMI were tremendously helpful here. We had all the constituents: we had NAMI, consumer, labor union, the legislators, three different divisions within the executive branch, somebody from the governor's office, somebody from the finance division, myself, and somebody from the capital building division. At the end, we had a unanimous vote that we needed to build a new state-of-the art mental health hospital to replace the two aged ones. In the meantime, over the two intervening years, we were working with our constituents and getting the legislature to make an assessment in community expansion so that we could downsize to get this single hospital to work.

In reframing the problem in a unique way, leaders create meaning for their organization. As Bennis and Nanus (1985) state, an essential factor of leadership is the leader's capacity to influence and organize meaning for the staff of the organization. Leaders take the facts and up-to-date information and come up with the know-why, rather than the know-how. Leaders understand why certain pieces of information are critical to their organization, not just how to use the information. In essence, leaders seek out information not just to know what new procedures to implement, but why the organization must move in a specific direction. Leaders use information to anticipate the future, not simply to manage the present. They understand trends that are suggested by the information.

> In reframing the problem in a unique way, leaders create meaning for their organization.

In CMHS's federal leadership role, the organization's mission was to transform the nation's mental health system toward a recovery-oriented system. As the leader of this initiative, Kathryn Power understood full well the importance of data and information in this change process. Kathryn recounted the challenge of getting out system transformation information in a meaningful way, and how important information is to continuing the transformation process.

> The difficulty for me is how to get ponderous information into a more palatable form, and then be able to talk about it in the simplest and most direct way…getting it into some sort of more digestible form that's palatable to congress and OMB. We know transformation is happening. It's just a matter of describing it in a way that will support the level of continuation that I think is necessary in order to continue transformation.

Jim Reinhard of Virginia reflected on the critical nature of data in terms of monitoring current service quality and outcomes, and its role in helping to anticipate the future.

> I think any success that I've had has been due to being able to take what data we have and to just stay on message; to use our information, whether it's the per capita expenditures in our community versus our institutions, or the research done on recovery. Decision makers and funders of the system must know that you're giving them data that's based on what you have, and is as accurate as you can make it. For example, with respect to reducing seclusion and restraint, we have made great strides in our facilities. We need to decide whether we can make another push to get it virtually eliminated. Everyone has significantly reduced seclusion and restraint, and there are several of our facilities that have eliminated it. Our data demonstrate that it can be done; now the question is what is the next step, especially in those facilities that have reached a plateau.

Pam Womack, who was interviewed when she was the executive director of a case management agency in Nashville, Tennessee, was adamant about obtaining information on how her agency was doing with respect to what they were supposed to be doing. Pam repeated the old adage, "When you are through changing, you are through." Pam sees information as the organization's capital that makes the change process more effective. The organization's information was derived from data that came from what people said was needed, or descriptive data that the agency routinely collected. For example, because their data indicated that new people needing services were not being seen quickly enough, and as a result were being lost from accessing services, they developed what they called the Bridge Program. The Bridge Program was linked to the case management team so that all new clients were seen immediately, so that housing was attended to, entitlements, such as food stamps applied for, clinic appointments made, etc., without delay. The initial implementation of the Bridge was not successful, so Pam changed its place in the organization and its leadership. She believed she could not hold allegiance to the plans if the data indicated that the original plan was not working.

Pam's organization had a set of key monitors that she made sure were summarized weekly. For example, they looked at the number of minutes a case manager was in face-to-face contact with consumers, hospitalization rates, where people were living, medications they were taking, etc. Pam could analyze figures by team; she made sure each team had access to this same information. Pam recounted that one goal was to spend at least 40% of the case managers' time in face-to-face contact. Initially one team couldn't hit the goal because they were not using their computers efficiently, so additional computer training was conducted. Another team had a disproportionate number of clients who needed extra time, so the complexion of this team was changed. As part of their leadership responsibilities, the case managers' supervisors go over the data weekly with their team.

> Even though the field of mental health seems to be regularly in an era of cost containment, leaders do not use information simply to contain costs or increase their organization's capacity to deliver more units of services at the same cost. For leaders, the information also is used to increase consumer benefits.

Even though the field of mental health seems to be regularly in an era of cost containment, leaders do not use information simply to contain costs or increase their organization's capacity to deliver more units of services at the same cost. For leaders, the information also is used to increase consumer benefits. While these consumer benefits also might decrease costs or change costs, leaders do not see cost containment as their only goal or as the most important priority. Using another example from Pam Womack, she said that she obtained information indicating that her agency's clients were not pleased with the hospital they used or with the emergency services. Other data indicated that people were going to the hospital only for a few days, so the leadership surmised that people did not really need the hospital because they were discharged so quickly. All of this information led to the development of a unique respite program. The respite program used local hotel rooms for consumers who needed to leave their homes during crisis. The agency rented a room at a local hotel for a person in a crisis. During people's stay at the hotel, typically they were supported by a recovering consumer who stayed with them at the hotel during the crisis. Pam stated that the creation of the respite program was an example of how the organization was constantly looking for information that showed whether procedures were a barrier or a help to a person's recovery. Pam amplified:

> Our whole goal is to remove any barrier that a consumer has to getting services here or to live their life…We ask, is this a barrier or a help? And then we just start lopping off the barriers.

Leaders think systematically about the information they receive in order to anticipate the future. Essentially, they explore, understand, and act upon the information (Carkhuff, 1971; Carkhuff & Benoit, 2005). In exploring the information, they try and take in as much information as possible, and categorize it in order to be able to better work with it. For example, they might seek out all the information on service interventions and categorize it by type of service, such as treatment, rehabilitation, crises intervention, self-help, etc. This wide net of information so categorized might help them see relationships between services that heretofore had gone unnoticed.

> Leaders think systematically about the information they receive in order to anticipate the future. Essentially, they explore, understand, and act upon the information

Larry Kohn was able to introduce the culture and practice of rehabilitation and recovery into a traditional treatment facility. Larry was introduced in previous chapters as the former director of services at the Center for Psychiatric Rehabilitation at Boston University. Larry also worked two evenings a week conducting a work issues' group at a private psychiatric facility. He was able to facilitate change at this organization even though he was not in a designated leadership position and was only there several evening hours a week. Larry's experience illustrates the point that change can be initiated by individuals at all levels of the organization; that information can change theoretical assumptions; and that the new information that elicits change can come not just from presentations or written materials, but from new experiences. Larry stated:

> I offer these three examples of ways in which new information helped to change the "treatment only" culture of the facility.
>
> Example one: Sharing personal information in the work issues group about my own career history, the struggles, difficulties, and setbacks as well as the successes, and asking other co-leaders to do the same, created an atmosphere of partnership and reciprocity critical to rehabilitation.
>
> Example two: I provided a steady flow of information about recovery in order to have participants connect their own experiences with others who have similar lived experiences. I also made certain that co-leaders listened to and read the same materials to balance their textbook, "treatment-only" approach to their work.
>
> Example three: The content of the work issues group focused on teaching skills and providing information on choosing, getting, and keeping school and work settings.
>
> The introduction of practical tools for regaining valued roles in the world complemented the importance of treatment gains. Planting the seeds at the facility for the successful juxtaposition of treatment and rehabilitation also required that I be aware of the conflicts that might arise as both participants and co-leaders grappled with the differences that they felt between my group and more traditional therapy groups. My belief that these two worlds could—and should—co-exist, always helped me to be able to explain and help guide people to see the differences as they were, and not as one approach being better or worse than the other. For example, I knew from listening to participants in these groups that they enjoyed that I shared personal experiences and personal information and encouraged co-leaders in my groups to do the same. At the same time, I knew that it was very important to not

polarize people by suggesting that this sharing was something that should happen in every group or something that every group leader needed to do. It was important for me to anticipate the felt discrepancy and be able to explain that every group leader had to choose for him- or herself how much disclosure they felt comfortable with by factoring in not only personal style, but also the nature of the group and the inherent differences in treatment goals versus rehabilitation goals.

Peter M. Senge (2006) talks about team learning as one of his five core disciplines for a learning organization. Team learning speaks to a leader-staff dialogue and an expectation that the team can suspend old assumptions and begin to form new thinking and work frameworks. Senge's belief is that team dialogues include understanding how certain traditional patterns of thinking interrupt learning new ways of performing and that these old and outdated patterns block new understanding and successful mastery of the current problems facing the organization. Senge's model challenges leaders to think in new ways, especially in areas, such as full integration of service users as key informants and the power inherent in the judicious use of self-disclosure about personal recovery experiences with people who do not know this potential exists.

Consistent with the thoughts of Senge, Pat Kramer, like Larry Kohn, also had to use information to have her staff see the complementary nature of initiatives that had heretofore been perceived by some to be mutually exclusive. When Pat Kramer was interviewed, she was associate director of community support services at Henderson Mental Health Center in Florida. Pat said she always was looking to make use of what she learned from the literature, consumer input, conferences, visits to other service programs, and networking. She saw information as the organization's capital for future change. Pat spoke in her interview about the development of two Assertive Community Treatment (ACT) teams designed to help in the downsizing of South Florida State Hospital. In this ACT demonstration, she married two seemingly disparate innovations about which she had heard: ACT and psychiatric rehabilitation technology. She reframed the issue, which some saw as using two competing models of change, to getting the most out of what she viewed to be complementary approaches. Some folks tried to dissuade her from using both approaches, in a sense lobbying for one approach over the other. Pat did not believe that consensus could be achieved. She obtained the resources to implement her view of the project. In her reframing of the issue she says she envisioned, "ACT as providing the structure of the program and the psychiatric rehabilitation technology as providing the soul." The strategy for implementing this change included using their previous agreement on mission and values and then pointing out that this "marriage of models" gave them a good chance of achieving their mission in a way compatible with values (Kramer et al., 2003).

As was pointed out earlier in this chapter, being able to understand what the information means is what separates leaders from other people. Leaders rely on their knowledge of themselves, their organization, their consumers, and other organizations to reframe the organizational problems and challenges. Typically before they act, leaders use their interpersonal skills to process the information with others. Using the strategy of get-give-merge-go that was mentioned in the previous chapter, leaders take the information they get and check out their understanding with the staff. It is at this point that leaders then act upon the information to change organizational practice in certain ways.

Basically, leaders use the information to improve personnel, program, and system features of their organization. Processing of information allows leaders to think organizationally, i.e., about their organization's mission; how that mission is expressed in terms of the organization's goals; how the organization's goals drive the interventions of the organization; how the policies and procedures guide the organization's interventions; how the organization's values are reflected in the interventions; and how the clinical processes and outcomes can be assessed.

> Leaders rely on their knowledge of themselves, their organization, their consumers, and other organizations to reframe the organizational problems and challenges.

Joan Erney of Pennsylvania spoke about how leaders had to be able to think "organizationally" for opportunities to initiate changes.

I think change is a good thing. I think change is positive, and my career history is reflective of that. But looking "for" change opportunities is different than when a change is thrust on you. In other words, leaders must constantly assess opportunities for change within their environment and take advantage of those opportunities. I think it is leadership's duty, when you are looking at routine information that is part of your daily work, that you know what the tea leaves are saying; you know your political environments and economic environments, and you understand where your power and influence is. Then, you are able to set the stage for needed change, with your vision leading your work.

> Leaders must constantly assess opportunities for change within their environment and take advantage of those opportunities.

Joan gave, as her example of a change initiative, her work to extend their behavioral health managed care program (Health Choices) from 25 counties to all 67 counties in Pennsylvania. Joan already had collected much of the information she needed to promote this change initiative.

I had visited all the county programs, state hospitals, and services areas in my first year, and I saw the continued theme of lost ground and lost opportunities because the Health Choices counties had access to Medicaid dollars and the opportunity to do cost effective alternatives. The Health Choices counties were able to develop psychiatric rehabilitation programs, community treatment teams, and all these really exciting services for folks that the non-choice counties could not. As a result, we laid out the plan to go statewide with Health Choices. I went out and talked to our constituents and our advisory committees to explain this plan and answer questions. I think an effective leader must set the stage for the conversation, to be willing to go out and talk about the vision, and then connect the vision to whatever the strategic plan is for that organization. It must all work together, or it will not make sense to others.

Joan continued her search for additional information to buttress the need for change.

While we were doing all this talking, I also was able to get staff to pull together our data. We were able to do a performance report on 25 counties without Health Choices versus the counties that were in the Health Choices Network. Our data reinforced our hopes; Health Choices offered real promise to our providers. We were able to show with real numbers that Health Choices supported the expansion of services to more people in programs, and that access was absolutely enhanced. We were able to show that instead of using long inpatient psychiatric stays, and inpatient drug and alcohol beds, we could shift our money and use more non-hospital, community services. Based on this information, we could envision an incredible expansion of cost effective, creative services that really support people's individual recovery plans, and a realigning of what works for real people receiving services. Through our data, we also were able to show an emphasis on quality, outcomes, and an improvement in the level of sophistication in the Health Choices counties.

Noteworthy is the fact that systematic thinking, processing of the information with others, and organizational planning also can produce serendipitous thoughts and unplanned directions for the organization. Leaders are comfortable with the idea that where they end up is not where they thought they would be when they began using the information. Remember how when Elizabeth Childs processed the data on hospital closure, the plan changed from closing one hospital to closing two aged hospitals, building one new hospital, and expanding community options.

When Charley Curie was at SAMSHA, he understood that changing information could change the leader's plans.

When I first came, I was trying to press a point that nothing should get in the way of people with co-occurring disorders getting the assessments and treatment that they needed. Most states were complaining that the block grant would not allow us to pay them for co-occurring services. I opened up the idea of taking a look at how we can make funding flexible, but then began to understand how threatening that was to the substance abuse field. I backed off from that because I was convinced that if I pressed that too hard, we would lose ground on being able to talk about co-occurring disorders. I think I was right, and today we are in a position that more money, not necessarily from the block grant but from other funding streams, is going to co-occurring disorders—which is helping the substance abuse field address the issues in the mental health field. From the public position I initially took, I changed. I think leaders must have information about their environment and figure out what will work out best in the long run, even if it means slowing something done or changing the goal.

Serendipity and systematic thinking are often partners in organizational change. In Mary Alice Brown's capacity as director of the Laurel Hill Center in Eugene, Oregon, she spoke about how she took advantage of opportunities, both planned and unplanned. As mentioned in chapter 2, the initiation of Laurel Hill's supported housing program was an obvious example. When the supported housing concept was being talked about nationally, their planning already had led them to develop a supported housing program. Then, unexpectedly, new funding became available that allowed Mary Alice to expand the supported housing program in a way she had not envisioned. The serendipitous emergence of new funding and the organization's systematic thinking about supported housing led Mary Alice to develop heretofore unplanned new models of supported housing.

> Serendipity and systematic thinking are often partners in organizational change.

Kathryn Power distinguished between managing and initiating change, and mentioned the necessity of each in the organizational change process. Kathryn maintained that an organization had to manage the basics of earlier changes as the organization initiated even more advanced levels of organizational change.

> This is not just a matter of managing change; this is a matter of initiating change, and that's much harder to do because as you initiate change, you have to manage previous changes as well. Then you have to initiate more change, and then you have to manage the new changes.

There are times, of course, that leaders must act to change their organization without all the information they believe they need. In these instances, as in all instances of decision making, leaders are guided by their values as well as the information they possess. In other words, they act in a manner consistent with their values even though the decision is not based on complete information. As a matter of fact, many decisions of mental health organizations need to be made before all the data are in. Leaders simply can't wait for the definitive, empirical, research-based evidence. In the mental health field, such proof is rare. What is not so rare, however, is an abundance of descriptive, correlational, and quasi-experimental research from which the leader must create meaning. Additionally, leaders need to set up systems to collect useful data. That does not mean that they should wait to make critical decisions, but it does mean that a lack of data relevant to a critical decision is also a call to action to get that data.

Leaders know that maintaining the status quo for too long is actually moving their organization backwards. Talking about change and planning about change for too long without acting can make leaders uncomfortable. For example, Larry Miller from Arkansas stated that talk sometimes lasts too long, and he needs to act even if consensus has not been achieved.

> Leaders know that maintaining the status quo for too long is actually moving their organization backwards.

> People will say, "Oh well, we could talk about this next month. Let's just continue to talk." I've often said we can continue to talk, but we also need to continue to act; these are peoples' lives we're responsible for and these things just can't wait. There could be some short term things we do and some longer term actions. I don't have a problem acting without consensus. I often tell people this is what I think we can do, and even if there's not total agreement, I say "unless you tell me I'm being totally ridiculous and off the wall, and that this can't be done, we need to do it."

But Larry also said that he didn't remain wedded to the plan of action.

> I also can change plans. Leaders need to be flexible and not be so entrenched or narcissistic that they cannot hear what other peo-

ple say if their plan isn't working. I think all too often there are people who once they've made up their mind, that's the way it has to be. I think that leads to trouble.

Leaders use different opportunities to "stay in touch" with the environment. Elizabeth Childs disclosed:

I still see some people in private practice, at home, on Saturdays. They keep me grounded. They remind me of what I am really trying to do. That it is really about the people who need the services; that they get what they need, and that they do get better. They go on to being incredible people. I'm always so admiring of these individuals. They have so much courage. They make me feel like it's a small thing that I do every day compared to what they do every day. I think it's about recognizing how hard they are of trying to live life with unbelievable odds. They really inspire me and remind me of the importance of humility. I try to get out as frequently as I can and talk to persons who are receiving services. Just recently an executive from one of the Medicaid health plans here in Massachusetts said to a colleague, "I can't believe that all these consumers and family members talk about the commissioner as though they know her. Why would they know her?" And my colleague said, "They do know her. She sits down and meets with them. They are as frequently in her office, more frequently in her office than the providers are." It's so important to stay close to the people who are your real constituents.

It is the leader's task to stay in touch with all the many sources of information. One person in the organization does not have to know about all the information that is available. Leaders may designate others to stay abreast of current subject areas. They then become internal resources to the leader and give information to the particular leader or leadership team that ultimately will be making the decision.

Renata Henry from Delaware was another leader who pays attention to data. She came to value information, even if it only came from one person, or was about one very specific point.

I have learned to expect and encourage feedback from our advocates. It took me a long time to see this, but I fully understand that they often see individual events as indicative of the entire system, when their constituency is an individual consumer, or a neighbor, or a friend. State office staff, including me, often look at these events as anomalies and outliers. It is easy to not pay as much attention as we should to these individual pieces of information as we come from this "macro system" place. However, I have worked really hard to understand this other, more individual specific kind of viewpoint. I understand its importance much more now than I did when I first came into this job. For example, now when an advocate calls with a complaint, that complaint is now elevated and becomes the most important issue that day. I, or one of my staff, follow-up on the issue and get back to the complainant. For me, if it's one complaint and that's all I get in a week, I'm happy. Trying to put myself in someone's shoes is really trying to make the argument for why their shoes are just as important as my shoes.

Leaders covet change even when things are going well for the organization. Effective and successful organizations have a culture that thrives on change. Leaders cannot allow the organization to rest on its laurels. Organizations that are at the leading edge of service provision prefer to see the next generation of services developed by themselves, not others. In other words, leaders prefer to leap frog their own leadership position themselves. Mary Alice Brown's development of the program to produce eyeglasses for the state of Oregon, and her combining supported housing and supported employment, are two examples. Likewise is Pat Kramer's marrying of ACT and psychiatric rehabilitation technology.

> Effective and successful organizations have a culture that thrives on change.

Innovative change occurs when the need or demand for a service is strong, and when the knowledge and the technology converge with the need. For example, the psychiatric rehabilitation services initiative was possible because consumers needed and demanded it, and at approximately the same time, the knowledge and technology finally became available to meet the need (Anthony, Cohen, Farkas & Gagne, 2002). Leaders, such as Dennis Rice and Pat Kramer, who incorporated psychiatric rehabilitation services into their organization did so not because they were considered unsuccessful at their present service capacity. Often the organizations that moved toward a psychiatric rehabilitation approach were the organizations that seemed to be relatively more effective already in comparison to other organizations.

Leaders seek the challenge of change. Leaders of effective organizations continually raise the bar or standard on which they wish to be judged. Mental health organizations are in the business of change—they seek to help consumers change. But organizational change seems to be harder than facilitating consumer change. Just as practitioners facilitate consumer change, leaders must facilitate organizational change—no matter how well the organization is doing currently. Thus Mary Alice Brown implemented two additional supported housing programs, even though the first supported housing program was successful.

> Just as practitioners facilitate consumer change, leaders must facilitate organizational change.

The employment of consumers of services in leadership positions in county, state, and federal service organizations was an innovation that fed off the need for change. Gayle Bluebird was a person with a psychiatric disability who described herself as someone who "thrived on change," and who recognized that "simply maintaining the status quo of an organization is actually moving the organization backwards." When Gayle was working full-time for the Department of Children and Families in Florida, she wanted to develop a Consumer Affairs Office at the district level in Broward County, so that there would be more opportunities, activities, and funding for the consumers of services. To create this change, Gayle reported that she:

> had to convince the administration of the value of such a position. Research was done and contacts were made in other areas of the country to obtain more information. Creating new positions is not easy in a bureaucracy. Even when you have the support, there is much resistance to change.

> I ultimately was given the opportunity to work as a monitor of involuntary treatment facilities and hospitals, using my background as a registered nurse, in exchange for time given to work

on developing an Office of Consumer Affairs. This was a workable solution. In due course, there was an office that had staff of director, myself, and five other full and part-time staff.

Gayle ruminated on the fact that when she initiated this change, she had not yet achieved consensus on this new direction; she was constantly working toward consensus for this change, even after the change had already occurred.

Leaders prefer to have other key staff agree with the direction in which they are changing. However, there are times when leaders must change a direction based primarily on their own understanding of the information. In general, leaders can tell, sell, or jell a new direction. By "jell," we mean achieve consensus on the particular change. However, leaders must discriminate when consensus is and is not necessary. Sometimes they may not even be able to sell or persuade their staff. At these times leaders, such as Pat Kramer or Larry Miller, may simply tell their staff about the impending change.

When Cynthia Barker, the director of the Project Phoenix mobile drop-in center in Tennessee was interviewed, she made the point that she had to discriminate when consensus was and was not necessary. Unlike Mike Hogan in Ohio, she was putting the vision forward almost by herself, and she was in a minority position with respect to the vision of a mobile drop in center. Cynthia remembered saying to herself, "...if this is my job we are going to do it my way." Cynthia believed there was a specific direction the project had to go to be consistent with the slowly emerging principles of self-help and consumer integration that were beginning to develop around the country. Cynthia recounted, "with respect to the 7-passenger van, as opposed to using the agency's 15-passenger vans,...this is the way it is going to be." Like Pat Kramer's unwillingness to wait for more definitive empirical data on the use of two different models simultaneously, Cynthia went with her values and the best information available.

Raul Almazar provided an example of how he needed to make a decision without consensus.

One of the things that I heard from staff and the majority of consumers is how weekends were very difficult and how there were a lot of power struggles in the morning. So I looked into it; it had to do with meal times and that the breakfast times on the weekends are the same as on weekdays because they had to be staggered. So consumers on a Saturday morning get awakened at 7:00 to go to the dining room to eat their breakfast so that the meal schedule works right. But then they get back to their unit with nothing to do until 9:00 or 9:30. The consumers were saying that they would like to sleep in, like other people, but that they were not allowed to because of the hospital policy.

So I made a decision that weekend breakfast policy was going to change. We made sure that people would get a nice heavy hot meal at lunch and brought a continental breakfast onto the unit on weekends; into the unit's nutrition rooms. We have microwaves and refrigerators; people now get a plate, they get their breakfast when they want it. I got significant, major opposition, such as "you're going to have cockroaches because you have more food on the unit; you know how expensive danishes are, as compared to oatmeal?" Basically I just told them I don't care; it's going to happen. It took about 4 months, and in that 4 months, I would get e-mails about "how this was still not working," or at meetings it would come up, "still not working." But now, a year and a half later, everyone is happy. And I use this as an example of how sometimes leaders just need to make decisions; hopefully the right decision, and in concert with their values."

Paolo del Vecchio had a relatively small staff of four people within the large federal SAMSHA organization. Nevertheless, Paolo was adamant in the necessity of leaders, no matter how small their staff, to embrace the principle of accessing and using information to bring about change, even when complete consensus had not occurred. To illustrate the significance of principle 7, Paolo used the example of leading SAMSHA's initiative in developing a consensus statement for SAMSHA and the entire services field with respect to the meaning of the concept of recovery.

The dimensions that were identified in the consensus statement included "respect, empowerment, safe and affordable housing, and taking control over your life." Of course, we have had pushback on the consensus statement, and we continue to get that.

We are trying to counter and change those coercive and stigma-based paradigms, not only within the mental health system, but even broader than that, our society at large. As you go against the traditions in mental health services, you're going to have this kind of resistance. It is critical to be persistent and use your own inner beliefs to continue to push these changes, particularly over the longer term.

Even when leaders must institute a change in their organization without consensus, that is not to say they have not involved their staff in the change process. Involvement and participation is possible without always relying on consensus. In her role as director of the Village in California, Martha Long had to sell, tell, or jell a new direction. As Martha told it, "some things are not negotiable." For example, 24-hour on call was a condition of employment and was not an option. Input was sought about how a 24-hour on-call system could operate within certain boundaries. At the time of Martha's interview, The Village had a procedure similar to HMOs where people could choose their own teams—essentially an open enrollment procedure. Martha wanted this to happen, but had to let it jell. Over time, the staff came over to this position, but she said she did not force it.

> In essence, leaders constantly plan for change.

In essence, leaders constantly plan for change. Their organizations expect change, and the staff of their organizations expect to be involved in the change process. While planning for change is good, simple allegiance to plans is not. Leaders who are comfortable with constant change understand that some plans may change even before they are implemented. What does not change, however, is the leader's commitment to change.

Leaders build their organization around exemplary performers.

- The leader directly exposes others to exemplars to maximize staff learning.

- The leader frees exemplars from organizational constraints so that exemplars can do what they do best.

- The leader recognizes that exemplars' initiative can be better modeled then taught didactically.

- The leader ensures exemplars have the organizational support they need.

- The leader understands that exemplars create opportunities for the entire organization.

- The leader leads rather than manages exemplars.

- The leader does not second guess the failures of exemplars.

- The leader understands that exemplars are strongly motivated by intrinsic rewards.

- The leader publicly recognizes the outstanding contributions of exemplars to the organization.

Leaders build their organization around exemplary performers.

Leaders are known by the followers they keep.

—*William A. Anthony*

We often forget that a key characteristic for a leader is to have followers! Without followers, the leader's ideas will have little effect. However, followers do not just follow. Followers must have a say about where they are being led. If a leader forgets this basic point, the leader will soon be without followers, especially the exemplary ones. It is the organization's exemplars that bolster the leader to lead effectively. While they may move on, eventually, to lead their own organization, exemplary staff seem to have organizational staying power. And the reason many exemplars stay is their leader.

The most important followers in an organization are the people who are considered exemplary. They are the models. They may be considered exemplary in how they manage a program or unit, how they themselves lead components of the organization, and/or their technical expertise. Regardless of the particular talent they bring to the organization, it is obvious to most that they possess unique talents. Effective and principled leaders also understand that their job is not necessarily to reassign exemplars to supervisory or management positions, unless that is the particular talent they possess. The leaders' task is to "turn exemplars loose," that is, to free them from unnecessary organizational constraints that inhibit them from acting on their talents. Additionally, leaders make sure exemplars know they have the support of the leaders.

Effective leaders also make sure that everyone else in the organization knows this as well. In Kim Ingram's attempts to transform the state institution in Thomasville, Alabama, into a true rehabilitation center, she relied on exemplary staff at all levels of the organization. She considered her new rehabilitation director exemplary, and when the rehabilitation director needed Kim's support for certain new rehabilitation initiatives, Kim made sure that her staff knew the rehabilitation director had Kim's total support.

Exemplars are unique in their ability to initiate new ideas, directions, and activities. They provide a unique source of variance to the organization. Exemplars create change within the organization itself. Whatever their unique talents, exemplars are similar in their ability to take risks and show initiative. When Mary Alice Brown built the outstanding optical program at Laurel Hill Center in Eugene, Oregon she freed an exemplary person in her organization to research and build the program. The work of this exemplar created opportunities for the entire organization with the income the optical program brought into the agency and the additional training opportunities for their clients.

> Exemplars are unique in their ability to initiate new ideas, directions, and activities.

At the Hogg Foundation in Texas, King Davis talked about the contributions of exemplary staff to certain initiatives within the organization.

> What I've done with that is to create leaders around particular areas. Let me give you an example. Our first priority, and our first effort at implementing our new priorities, was around integrated healthcare. We really tasked Laurie and the two or three members of her team with making that happen. But rather than my assuming the presence or the face of the foundation for this work, we really tasked her with the responsibility. First off, we asked her to interact with all of the key national leaders on this project, only bringing Linda Frost or me in, as needed. We also tasked her with the responsibility of putting together the RFP team. We asked her to take on the responsibility of interacting with, and contracting with, prospective evaluation teams. She contracted for the training, and we tasked her with the responsibility of making a variety

of presentations in various places around the country for this initiative. And when that was all done, we asked her to make presentations to our staff. We also asked her to identify the various members of her working team, from our secretarial staff to the staff
that are responsible for the public relations, to the evaluation staff,
to the information technology staff, the human resources staff,
and the contractors as well. We also built in some processes where
those individuals were recognized for the work that they did. We
made sure that we recognized the extraordinary work exemplars
do. And it said to other staff that "your work will be recognized
by people within the organization for its quality and impact."

Besides supporting exemplars within the organization, and
besides freeing exemplars to perform, leaders try to use exemplars
to create additional exemplars within the
organization. Unfortunately, *personal initiative* is difficult to teach. Leaders, therefore,
try to expose other staff in the organization
to the exemplars' thinking and actions. Fortunately, initiative can be learned through
modeling. Other staff can learn to be exemplars by watching and working with their
exemplary colleagues. As discussed in a previous chapter, Bob
Williams, superintendent of Florida State Hospital, ensured that
exemplars learned from other exemplars when he identified the
exemplars within his organization and formed them into his leadership group as new positions opened up. His exemplary leadership team learned from one another.

> Fortunately, initiative can be learned through modeling. Other staff can learn to be exemplars by watching and working with their exemplary colleagues.

In Colorado, Sandy Forquer referred to her exemplars as "product champions." Some of her exemplars

> were buried in their agencies. We asked folks to recommend peo-
> ple to serve on major committees who had energy, were respect-
> ed by their peers, and had demonstrated past or potential leader-
> ship. They become critical to making things happen. We have
> invested dollars in training these product champions. I also select-
> ed exemplary people from outside Colorado to join us or consult
> to our organization.

Why do exemplars remain with their leaders? It is more than just how leaders permit exemplars to function within the organization. In order to remain a follower, the followers themselves need to confer leadership to the leader. When the leader lives out the principles suggested in this text, exemplary followers are encouraged to stay around. It is a regular occurrence, in mental health organizations as well as business organizations, that when the leader leaves, within the next six months, the exemplars in the organization also begin to leave. The bond between leaders and exemplars is strong, often stronger than the bond between exemplars and the organization. A dramatic example of exemplars following the leader out of an organization occurred when mental health commissioner Richard Surles left New York State due to a change in gubernatorial leadership. His exemplars were gobbled up by organizations around the country, including private managed behavioral health care organizations, advocacy organizations, state mental health departments, and universities.

> The bond between leaders and exemplars is strong, often stronger than the bond between exemplars and the organization.

One of Richard Surles exemplary employees was David Shern, whose comments on exemplars occur later in this chapter. As recounted by Richard:

> One of the things I felt best about doing in New York was developing the role that David Shern played. One of the things I said to David is "you've got to change how you act here." We've got eight major interventions that we're trying to put in place, and I have about three to four years to do it. You've got to have an outcomes measurement strategy attached to these issues. You can do some of the other things you want to; but I want you studying whether or not intensive case management is effective; whether or not comprehensive psychiatric services make a difference, etc. We lined up our research and our studies and our data collection around our mission. As we would get into year two, or year three, we'd have this fantastic data to roll out to the governor and the legislature to support the shifts we were trying to make. Relevant to this point is that good leaders don't own solutions. Exemplary

people take responsibility for creating solutions, like a David Shern, who became a real asset to the organization. They were the stars. Rightly, they were the ones that got credit for taking the initiative and running with it. My role, in most of these activities, was that I can say now that I probably was the person that created the idea and created the environment for it to happen, but then I got the hell out of the way.

Some of the conversations that take place between leaders and their exemplars are something to behold. These verbal exchanges are much more than a give and take discussion, where each participant tries to defend his or her own position. The conversations are exploratory, designed to stake out new ground and to create new possibilities. When a leader and her or his exemplars engage in such a dialogue, there is a commitment to a truthful reality and an as yet unknown future.

> Exemplars and the leaders for whom they work seem to be motivated as much by intrinsic rewards as by extrinsic rewards.

Effective leaders treat their exemplars as if they were volunteering to work in the organization. By that we mean that exemplars and the leaders for whom they work seem to be motivated as much by intrinsic rewards as by extrinsic rewards. Exemplars feed off the leaders' enthusiasm, excitement, and passion for the vision. They choose to work for outstanding leaders, and their rewards often are more internal than external. Len Stein's pathfinding vision of community-based treatment for people with the most serious disabilities was built by exemplars who shared his vision. It would be safe to say that Len worked with a cast of exemplars who carried this vision around the country and the world.

> What distinguishes exemplars is the passion they bring to their work, an enthusiasm and excitement born of commitment to a cause larger than themselves, and an organizational vision that is headed in the direction of their personal vision.

Exemplars do not simply agree with their leader's wishes and direction. They commit to them. As a matter of fact, at times they may disagree vehemently with the leader on certain points. Nor do exemplars simply resign themselves to the leader's direction. What distinguishes exemplars is the passion they bring to their work, an enthusiasm and excitement born of commitment to a cause larger than themselves, and an organizational vision that is headed in the direction of their personal vision. Exemplars stand out by virtue of their commitment and their passion.

Larry Miller from Arkansas reminded us of the difficulty in rewarding exemplary staff in a state mental health system that is resource poor and has barriers to using cash incentives and rewards that are common in the private sector.

> Exemplars stand out by virtue of their commitment and their passion.

> It is not all about money. I always tried to recognize people at meetings if something good was going on. I would give extra attribution to that. One of the other things we did was to have "seclusion and restraint celebration" if a unit did a particularly good job in not using S/R in a particularly difficult situation. We would broadcast around the hospital when a mental health technician or a particular nurse did a particular good intervention with a patient and achieved a successful outcome; a near miss. Another example is a relatively symbolic monetary award for the nursing staff, that is called "nurse of the month," whereby the nurse manager's put money in a pot and the monthly winner gets it.

Larry searches for people within the organization who are exemplary; he did not manage them but supported them through such things as additional training, memberships, and mentoring.

Carlos Brandenburg from Nevada recognized both the importance and difficulty in rewarding exemplary performers.

> I knew that in a state system I couldn't reward them monetarily. I didn't have the ability to say "I'm going to give you a five percent raise for doing such an outstanding job." But we do a lot of other things. We have an employee of the month and those names go on a plaque. We have recognition events for these great employees of the year. We afford great employees to have parking spaces close to the hospital where they work. And they are the only ones who are allowed to do that. A lot of times you go into a state hospital or other state organization and you will see a parking sign that says, "Dr. Brandenburg, Commissioner." We don't do that.

Basically, I don't allow any of the agency directors to have preferential parking. The only one that has preferential parking is the employee of the month or the employee of the year. We also do proclamations—we've been able to do state proclamations for employees. We recognize them at events. We go out of our way to recognize folks. And now all of my agency directors elevate their outstanding employees through recognition, through proclamations, through memos—whatever we can to basically tell folks that this guy or this woman has done an outstanding job for us and we want to recognize that. But I think a lot of the recognition, too, goes to just the empowerment. I mean, we want our staff to feel that they can make a difference. We're not so crystallized and galvanized that we won't change. If our staff see things that we can do differently, I encourage all of my staff to tell me so that we can do it better.

Shortly after Richard Surles left New York State, David Shern headed south to a deanship at the University of South Florida's Mental Health Institute. It then became David's job to make sure his top performers or exemplars were recognized in his new position. David reflected:

What I always tried to do was not only tell them how fantastic they were doing, but to tell them that what they were doing was exactly what we wanted them to do. This makes it sound as though my behavior was very conscious, but it really was not; it was just a way to connect with people. Of course the very, very best people were hitting all of their targets. They were developing research programs; they were bringing nine million dollars in external support. They were running three federal centers; two or three state centers. At every opportunity, I commended them and tried to reward them for the extraordinary work they were doing. They, in turn, also recognized their own people in staff meetings, in a like manner.

The work of exemplars is celebrated by their leaders. As was detailed in a previous chapter, leaders strive for a positive relationship with all their staff, and most certainly their exemplars. Ineffective, new, or uncertain leaders often are threatened by the emergence of exemplars. Unwise leaders think exemplars are trying to take their job. Effective and principled leaders believe that exemplars who take over parts of the leaders' job will free these leaders to reach for new heights. Just as leaders free exemplars to do better, exemplars free leaders to take the organization to greater accomplishments. And leader mentoring of exemplars can work toward successful succession planning also. One of us (KH) found several exemplary staff when she took her position as assistant hospital administrator at Memorial Regional Hospital's Behavioral Health Center in Hollywood, Florida. Kevin related that:

> Unwise leaders think exemplars are trying to take their job. Effective and principled leaders believe that exemplars who take over parts of the leaders' job will free these leaders to reach for new heights.

three exemplars, Tammy Tucker, Joyce Myatt, and Marcy Smith, were able to make tremendous progress in moving the Memorial Healthcare System's behavioral health services forward. They were creative, person centered, and individually driven to create best practice supports and services for the children and adults we were serving. Within three years, a 24-hour, state-of-the-art psychiatric emergency service was established, as well as a community mental health outpatient center that Joyce took the lead on. Residential and outpatient services for children were expanded as were substance abuse services. Marcy, the lead psychologist was able to integrate her work into much of the other hospital general services, including the children's hospital, and this integration added much to the general hospital's staff "valuing" what we did. Our small leadership team would meet individually and as a group as often as necessary to dialogue about goals, dreams, and plans in moving the organization forward, always remembering that we were part of a much larger and well-regarded system of care. We would all take turns attending community mental health stakeholder meetings to keep on top of what the service users, families, and other providers needed. Sometimes we all disagreed and would argue, but much more as colleagues than as "supervisor and staff." When I left this position my succession planning was taken care of and Tammy Tucker, seamlessly, took over my position.

And last, without the support of Frank Sacco, CEO of the entire healthcare systems, and Ken Hetledge, hospital administrator, who were my supervisors and who are visionary leaders in their own right, this work could not have been done. I think now, in retrospect, that perhaps I was one of their exemplars—and they definitely served as my mentors.

At Thresholds in Chicago, Tony Zipple understood the importance of supporting exemplary staff and trusting their decision-making abilities.

You need to have staff who are better at their jobs than you would be. When I got to Thresholds, everyone looked to me to decide almost everything that mattered. Not only can I not do that for an organization this complex, but it is unwise to try. If my program leaders were not better at services, my HR staff not better on labor issues, my IT staff not better at information systems than I am, then we would never be a very competent organization! You need to have confidence in your staff. For example, we needed to make a mission-critical decision about a new electronic medical record. The team, led by our director of information systems, got the right people in the room. Quality, programs, accounting, etc., developed the process, did the research, and made the decisions. Granted I had set some parameters for the process and decisions upfront, and in the end, I needed to sign off, but after all the very competent work that they did to reach a decision, I was really signing off on their work, sponsoring them, rather than deciding.

Exemplars cannot be micromanaged. Managing exemplars is an oxymoron. Leaders and exemplars have a relationship built on empathy and trust. Exemplars know in their hearts that their leader not only believes in them, but also is constantly promoting them both within and outside the organization. Promotion in this context does not mean simply promoting exemplars up the organizational chart. What it does mean is promoting exemplars, to others, by publicly recognizing the unique and outstanding contribu-

> Exemplars cannot be micromanaged....
> Leaders and exemplars have a relationship built on empathy and trust.

tions they make. Scott Graham, in his position as executive director of two rehabilitation agencies in Florida and Maryland, tried to hire people whom he thought had the potential to become exemplars, and then recognized them for their efforts. As an example, Scott talked about a part-time employee who had "great interpersonal skills and common sense"; an exemplar in the making. He convinced this individual to come to work full time. Over time, she became a supervisor and then director of human resources.

Principled leaders are trying constantly to get the right people in the right positions, either through new hiring, position changes or revised positions. They understand that the organizational train is going nowhere unless the people in charge of the organizational processes can drive the train. Exemplars will not drive their processes in different directions, because the organization's vision, mission and values align their separate tracks. There will be no head on collisions—races perhaps—but not organizational train wrecks.

> [Principled leaders] understand that the organizational train is going nowhere unless the people in charge of the organizational processes can drive the train.

Linda Rosenberg, executive director of the National Council for Community Behavioral Health, spoke about the importance of exemplars in most all her organization's leadership roles. To her, exemplars made the organization effective for the immediate term and were critically important for the future.

> I start from principle 8 as probably the principle I'm most conscious of in terms of leadership. You're only as good as the people around you. I think as a leader your job is to have great people and let them shine. It is also your responsibility as well, that when you leave a leadership position, there's always someone right behind you who can fill it. Your board may not go the way you wanted with respect to choosing the next leader, but as the current leader, you work to prepare people to be ready; where it's a natural for them to be qualified to ascend. I'm very proud that I can say that wherever I've worked, that's been the case. For example, when I came to NCCBH as director, we had someone who was working in human resources, and she had tremendous social skills. So it made sense for her to be our membership per-

son. Also, in my current position, I've been able to hire outstanding people. Chuck Ingolia, I think, is fabulous. I just hired Kara Sweeney as our membership director; I mean really very talented people who have the potential certainly to step up. They won't necessarily all stay here forever because we're a very small central staff. But I don't mind that. I think that's a good thing. I want people to have great opportunities in their life. When I was in New York, I had been senior deputy commissioner; the person who was my deputy is now the senior deputy commissioner, Bob Hyers. I take credit for that; not for his talent, that's his—but for spotting him and for having a succession plan. I think that's what a succession plan really is; it's hiring and grooming people in your organization. You get the credit for how smart they are; you were smart enough to bring them with you or to hire them. I think principle 8 is a very important principle.

In Connecticut, Thomas Kirk extended the concept of exemplary staff to exemplary organizations, and used these organizations as models for other organizations in the state. At one time Connecticut had something called a "giraffe award," given to individuals or organizations that were willing to stick their neck out and take a chance on a new initiative. Thomas gave an example of a giraffe.

It was a general hospital just like any other, and they had an emergency room based in the Bridgeport area. They were willing to set up a peer outreach approach where peers were trained to be part of their emergency department staff. When this first came up, most people said, "I'll believe that when I see it. Add peers to emergency department staff and expect them all to get along and work together?" But the hospital went forward, developed formal training with a group from Yale for the peer employees, and they became part of the ER staff. When people presented at the emergency room with psychiatric emergencies or some other type of behavioral disorder, the peer staff served to make it less stressful for those persons and for the emergency department staff. They often were instrumental in having the person stay with them in their office, before ER staff saw them. This program reduced the wait time in the emergency department, by many hours, from what it had been previously. This program also looked at the environment of care issues and fixed up a specific area with better furniture and carpeting, etc. There was music and all sorts of other kinds of things that served to make it a less stressful place. This was clearly a "before-its-time program," that used many of the principles of trauma informed care that we now hear about a lot. We were really surprised, back then, to have a hospital jump in to do this. I didn't think it was going to work at all. And now a couple of other hospitals have done this also.

Next, under Thomas Kirk's leadership in Connecticut, his staff created the "Centers of Excellence" program. This program was based on the assumption that exemplary organizations, just like exemplary performers, would be motivated to achieve excellence through non-monetary intrinsic rewards and public recognition.

The Centers of Excellence program allowed us to identify certain areas that we really wanted to put a premium on. One of them might be cultural competency, one might be peer services, one might be co-occurring disorders, and one of them might be innovative outreach procedures. One of the things we do, again going back to exemplary performers, we put out a bid for agencies to suggest why they should be a Center of Excellence. We were of the opinion that we were likely to get few, if any, responses because we weren't offering them any new money. What we did offer was technical assistance and recognition of being a Center of Excellence.

The first time we went out with the Centers of Excellence proposal, I think we had something in the range of 16 to 20 agencies that jumped at the chance. Then we added additional topics to the table, and it became much more competitive. A healthy competition I think, but competition nonetheless, such as, "Why did that agency get this distinction, we are doing just as well, how can we be included?" And it's just one of those examples, I guess, similar to finding ways to recognize exemplary staff in exemplary agencies. And some of these folks are great in some areas, but maybe not so much in others. For instance, an agency might not be great on administrative functions, but is an agency that is doing way beyond average work to provide community-based support services in a person-driven framework.

Staff who are exemplars because of their technical expertise often will grow beyond their leader's technical skills. Effective leaders need to grow as leaders so that they do not experience their exemplars' technical expertise as a threat. Leadership skills and technical skills are not mutually exclusive. But leaders do find, particularly those who achieved leadership positions initially through their technical expertise, that they must sometimes take the effort to expand their leadership capacity by taking time and resources away from their technical development. As their leadership demands mount, effective leaders can be *pulled* between their need to expand their technical skills or their leadership skills. Technical exemplars within their own organization allow the technical aspects of the organization to grow along with the leader's skills of leadership. Scott Graham looked for people "smarter than me" to ensure that the organizational technical expertise would continue to grow.

> Effective leaders need to grow as leaders so that they do not experience their exemplars' technical expertise as a threat.

> Technical exemplars within their own organization allow the technical aspects of the organization to grow along with the leader's skills of leadership.

Gayle Bluebird from Florida recounted how she worked in several positions that involved consumer leadership. She let her exemplars use their special talents and supported them organizationally. Because of these exemplars Gayle thought her leadership skills were enhanced.

> Being a person with a disability myself meant that I needed to be able to share what my limitations are, in such a way, that I could still be a good leader. It was important to me to have other good "communicators" work with me; people who could relate well to people we were serving. I was capable of teaching communication skills and techniques, but in other areas I did not have skills, such as good technical or reasoning skills. Choosing people who would complement me was important. In my last position, I had an assistant who had terrific computer skills and was also very loyal. She could have been in a different job, and in fact, had

made much more money in a previous but unrelated job. She had a physical disability that prevented her from pursuing jobs in her field. In many ways, working for me was perfect for her as she was able to secure some needed accommodations that may not have been possible elsewhere. Leadership in this case necessitated my supporting her talents and abilities and allowing her to be the leader in her specialty areas. I believe we were positive role models for each other. Between us we were able to serve people effectively.

One of us (KH) worked with Gayle Bluebird and provided an example of Gayle and another colleague as an exemplary employees.

What folks really need to understand about Gayle Bluebird is her unswerving focus on creating systems of care that are recovery-oriented and her incredible creativity. Gayle started the consumer-run art center for Broward County in Florida, when I was the alcohol, drug abuse and mental health district program Supervisor there. That program received state and national recognition. Gayle also started the Consumer Advocacy Team that did participatory dialogues with consumers and staff in that county as part of the state's involuntary commitment, performance improvement process. Years later, Gayle then took on the task of helping the administration of Atlantic Shores (now GEO Care, Inc.)/South Florida State Hospital when they decided to eliminate seclusion and restraint. Gayle, almost single-handedly, developed the comfort rooms there and had much to say about why conflict was occurring on the units in the first place. She also provided debriefing services to the person's being served, throughout the hospital. Gayle, and her colleague Tom Lane, were instrumental in the incredible improvements in services that occurred during my tenure at that hospital. I think all I did was trust both of them, let them go, and advocate for them when things got "sticky" as they sometimes did. Gayle and Tom are now nationally recognized leaders and are doing their work in multiple states; I only can say that my small role was sometimes providing support and a safe political buffer for Gayle and Tom; neither needed much more than that.

All the leaders of exemplars discussed in this chapter gave their exemplary followers some combination of support, trust, freedom, recognition, and/or at times, protection. What they did not do was tell them exactly how to do what they do! Paradoxically, the presence of exemplars can both threaten and

> Leaders who see exemplars as an opportunity for both themselves and their organization will grow their organization as well as themselves.

support their leaders. Leaders who see their exemplars as a threat will neither develop nor retain exemplary staff. Leaders who see exemplars as an opportunity for both themselves and their organization will grow their organization as well as themselves. Exemplary followers can outperform their leaders. Principled leaders make sure their exemplary followers can.

Conclusion

Good leaders can be born and made—being born is the more mysterious part.

—William A. Anthony

We know little about conceiving leaders. Obviously, the genetics of leadership was not the topic of this book! However, identifying effective leadership principles that can directly lead to the development of leadership competencies is becoming less mysterious.

People can and do learn. Leaders can and do learn. The leaders who spoke about their experiences for this book are still learning. Much of what they are learning concerns "themselves" in relationship to the "tasks of leadership." As pointed out by Kouzes and Posner (2002), leadership development is ultimately about self-development. Musicians may have their instruments, and engineers may have their computers, and accountants may have their calculators, but leaders only have themselves. They are, in fact, their own instruments. It could be that the path for leaders is akin to workforce self-actualization, and if so, that may be why leadership development has been so hard to pin down or describe.

Bennis and Nanus (1985) believe that the leaders' capacity to develop and improve their own performance and outcomes is what distinguishes leaders from followers. Leaders know who they are and where they are going, and they build a workforce that will help get them there. While leaders have their eyes on the vision, their ears are focused on themselves and their environment. They listen, and they learn from their successes and failures; and they continue to develop.

Terry (1993) makes the point that leaders must not engage in self-deception. As Gardner (1995) states, leaders must embody the traits that are part of the vision or the story they are conveying. If leaders become out of touch with themselves, their followers will eventually become out of touch with their leaders.

Bolman and Deal (1995), in their book titled *Leading with Soul,* believe that successful leaders embody their followers' most precious values and beliefs. They suggest that leaders help their followers to see that they [the followers] are doing something worth doing, something significant that makes the world a better place. Mental health leaders should be able to provide their followers what these authors call "the gift of significance." By its very nature, mental health work should provide meaning to the people working in these positions, and leaders need to make sure that the significance of this work is not lost.

> By its very nature, mental health work should provide meaning to the people working in these positions, and leaders need to make sure that the significance of this work is not lost.

Terry (1993) expands on the concept of the leaders' courage. In particular, Terry talks about how a courageous leader can challenge the fear of diversity within the workplace, be it diversity in experience, personality, class, gender, etc. Bringing various frames of reference to the table can make the leaders' work more challenging and more significant. Conflict that emerges from diversity will be seen by effective leaders as an opportunity rather than simply a threat. In this way, conflicts will be utilized to move forward, rather than simply managed.

In Kouzes and Posner's first edition of *The Leadership Challenge* (1987), they described personal dimensions of leaders, such as enthusiasm, excitement, passion for the dream, competence, and being forward looking, honest, and inspirational. Their summary leadership concept, under which all these other characteristics were grouped, was the concept of credibility. A later book by these two authors was devoted entirely to the issue of leadership credibility (Kouzes & Posner, 1993). In essence, they believe that in order for the leaders' message to be received, the leaders must be credible themselves. Credi-

> Credibility is a characteristic that leaders must constantly earn.

bility is a characteristic that leaders must constantly earn. Like other authors on leadership, they imply that continued credibility is a function of the leaders' constant self-development.

COMMITMENT, CREDIBILITY, CAPACITY

In reflecting on the leaders interviewed for this book, it is interesting to note how differently they present themselves. Obviously, they represent variety in demographics, i.e., age, gender, academic credentials, etc. Some come across more analytical than others, some more energetic, others more emotional, others more insightful. But what of the similarities? To us, there seem to be three. Mental health leaders universally seem to be characterized by commitment, credibility, and capacity.

As a group, they seem to be unequivocally committed to a vision. While the essentials of the vision vary from leader to leader, the commitment does not. Some may express the commitment more forcefully, or more energetically or more passionately than others. But there is a determination; a very present persistence in doing what one can to achieve the vision. While the leaders must work on developing themselves in order to

> Mental health leaders universally seem to be characterized by commitment, credibility, and capacity.

achieve the vision, their commitment is to something bigger than themselves. The self-development of leaders is in service to their commitment to the organizational vision.

Secondly, the leaders are similar in that they all possess credibility. There is validity to their leadership that is bestowed upon them by their staff. By definition, one cannot be a leader without followers. And it is followers who have to listen to leaders. Followers often are willing to concede to their leaders based on the leaders' credibility. While followers present their own opinions, argue their case, and suggest different directions, at some point they must be willing to agree or compromise and then stand firmly with their leaders.

Lastly, the leaders interviewed for this text seem to possess the capacity for leadership. Their core activities were in agreement with many of the basic principles of leadership, as described in this text. Each leader interviewed identified, most strongly, with different combinations of these principles. Some championed certain principles over others. Some stressed that certain principles were more important, at different times, in their own development or in their organization's development. Many had leaders, within their own organizations, who acted consistently with some of these principles and the leaders interviewed recognized this leadership capacity in their own staff.

> Leaders who have leadership commitment, credibility, and the capacity to make change, have a better chance of making their vision last.

Leaders who have leadership commitment, credibility, and the capacity to make change, have a better chance of making their vision last. In the mental health field there are competing visions and stories. The mental health leaders in this text attempted to communicate to their staff and embody their vision. In order to have their vision prevail, their vision must supplant, suppress, complement, or in some ways be more telling than previous or current other visions (Nanus, 1992).

This book has looked forward and backward. Some of the leaders mentioned in this text began their leadership story in the late 1960s and early 1970s, before the mental health field's general acknowledgment that recovery was more than a dream. Others achieved leadership status very recently and are continuing in their leadership roles. However, we cannot go forward as leaders without also understanding past leadership contributions. As Terry (1993) discusses, our vision of the future is a vast as our understanding of the past. We can envision our future by respecting the past. Reading about past and current mental health leadership activities broadens our understanding of the future of leadership.

In writing this text, we did not start with any preconceived theory about leadership. We tried to let the leaders' experience create the content. However, if you compare the core principles and tasks that emerged in *Principled Leadership* with those that were emerging in the leadership literature, it becomes clear that the leaders highlighted in this book were practicing the art and science of principled leadership.

AN OVERVIEW OF CURRENT LEADERSHIP LITERATURE

Many thoughtful scholars have written about leadership and its legends, myths, theories, and principles (Bass, 1990; Den Hartog & Koopman, 2001; Conger, 1999; Lorenzi, 2004; Van Mart, 2003; Rooke & Torbert, 2005; Shamir & Howell, 1999). However, the question of what has been learned, demonstrated to be effective, and is transferable from business to other settings remains a debated subject. As stated in the introduction of this book, and advanced as one of the reasons for writing *Principled Leadership,* most of the literature on leadership has been centered in the corporate for-profit world, the field of education, and organizational psychology. As such, it is incumbent upon mental health policy makers and providers to visit this literature, not to find perfect answers, but so as not to re-invent the wheel. History does tend to repeat itself. To believe that the tenets and principles of leadership are conscripted by any one discipline, profession, or setting is to miss an opportunity to learn from the entire range of leadership literature.

> To believe that the tenets and principles of leadership are conscripted by any one discipline, profession, or setting is to miss an opportunity to learn from the entire range of leadership literature.

One of the most notable research projects on leadership included a comprehensive analysis of transformational, transactional and laissez-faire leadership styles (Judge & Piccolo, 2004). Transformational leadership was defined as a style that focuses on meeting the higher order needs of followers through the use of charisma, inspirational motivation, intellectual stimulation, and individualized follower considerations. The transactional leadership style was described as one that gives followers something in exchange (contingent rewards) for their work, in terms of resources and as a quid-pro-quo relationship. Transactional leaders are either active or proactive through supervision, consistent monitoring, and timely intervention, or passive in terms of responses predicated on emerging problems. Finally, a type of non-leadership style was discussed, identified as laissez-faire leadership. This latter is characterized by behaviors that include a "failure to make decisions, hesitation in taking action, and being absent when presence is required" (Judge & Piccolo, 2004, p. 755–756).

From 1990 to 2003, during the time that many of the principled leaders referenced in this book were practicing, transformational leadership became the major topic in the leadership literature (Judge & Piccolo, 2004). The evidence seemed to conclude that this type of leadership, relative to other types of leadership, produced higher levels of performance from employees on variables, such as job satisfaction, satisfaction with the leader, motivation, organizational performance, and believed leader effectiveness (Judge & Piccolo, 2004).

According to Den Hartog & Koopman (2001), an approach called the "new leadership" has fueled a renewed interest in leadership literature that has tired of simple trait and style definitions. What has emerged is a clear emphasis on a transformational leadership style that also includes the characteristics of the transactional style. Furthermore, this "new leadership" incorporates charismatic qualities that do not necessarily dominate but are available when needed. In essence this new model of transformational leadership includes charisma as an important quality to be used, as needed, in concert with typical employer-employee transactional negotiations. This new combined theory attempts to explain how certain leaders are able to "achieve extraordinary levels of follower motivation, admiration, commitment, respect, trust, dedication, loyalty, and performance" (Den Hartog & Koopman, 2001, p. 173).

> In this book, we stop short of categorizing principled leaders by traits or styles, instead preferring to explicate their actions and the principles that the leaders interviewed for this book believe guided their performance of certain tasks.

We believe the principles and tasks identified in *Principled Leadership* explain the accomplishments of these leaders without, at this time, resorting to a theoretical explanation. It is true that many of the examples in *Principled Leadership* resonate with the transformational leadership descriptions. However, in this book, we stop short of categorizing principled leaders by traits or styles, instead preferring to explicate their actions and the principles that the leaders interviewed for this book believe guided their performance of certain tasks.

Many writers have noted that transformational leadership arises in times of organizational crisis; often a high-impact situation that arises unexpectedly and threatens the viability of the organization as it exists (Burns, 1978; Shamir & Howell, 1999). As described in the introduction, the entire mental health system and many of the organizations within this system are in crisis, due in part to the transformative power of the recovery vision, a rapidly developing knowledge base, the emergence of additional services, such as psychiatric rehabilitation, new organizational structures, and changing financing requirements, etc.

Traditional leadership literature depicts effective leader behaviors in crisis situations in a way that reaffirms the behaviors of mental health leaders illustrated in *Principled Leadership*. For example, Shamir and Howell (1999) state that leadership activities to address a *crisis* often start with a leader's idealized vision of what needs to be done and progress to implementation, given the followers ability to accept and participate in the change process. Usually this situation is linked to conditions described as "weak," meaning that the organization is experiencing a high degree of change, does not have clearly identified outcomes, and cannot yet link specific performance objectives to clear goals. These organizational situations require extraordinary efforts by both leaders and followers; are characterized by the need to redefine the status quo; and require the kind of leadership that creates hope, new opportunities, and faith that these can occur. (Shamir & Howell, 1999).

> Leadership and management roles are clearly described as important but very different; in fact, the most widely quoted phrase still used today is, "Managers are people who do things right; leaders are people who do the right thing." (Bennis & Nanus, 1985, p. 221).

For several decades the leadership literature has focused on the distinction drawn between leadership and management. As touched on in the introduction, many scholars argue that these two functions are very different in scope, tasks, and measurable outcomes. These arguments define leadership as "influencing others, creating a vision for change and holding people accountable" (Spillane, Halverson & Diamond, 2004; National Executive Training Institutes, 2007). They define management as accomplishing tasks and managing routines within an organizational structure. Thus, leadership and management roles are clearly described as important but very different; in fact, the most widely quoted phrase still used today is, "Managers are people who do things right; leaders are people who do the right thing" (Bennis & Nanus, 1985, p. 221).

Classic literature on the leadership/management distinction suggests that while there is overlap in the function and roles between leaders and managers, and some managers do emerge as leaders in their work, management is ultimately about "seeking order and stability" (Spillane et al., 2004). Leadership is focused on seeking adaptive and constructive change for survival and growth (Spillane et al., 2004). Understanding and successfully implementing tremendous organizational change, such as that called for in the report of the President's New Freedom Commission on Mental Health (2003), will require both leaders and managers to have key roles (Lorenzi, 2004). As noted previously, we view these leader and managerial roles as not mutually exclusive; leaders emerge from management while leaders also manage at times.

Relevant to the notion of principled leadership is the description of an applied theory called "Prosocial Leadership" (Lorenzi, 2004). The author identifies the fact that, in his opinion, leadership must be defined by morality and must demonstrate actions for the common good. In *Principled Leadership,* the leaders' pursuit of the common good is reflected in the overarching vision of helping more people recover from serious mental illnesses. Lorenzi notes that some leadership models and definitions do not discriminate between moral and immoral leader types. Lorenzi includes morality as mandatory in his definition of leadership" and defines this to be a "systemic, purposeful influence" that is "widely acknowledged by the broad constituency as an outcome with primarily, if not exclusively, beneficial effects" (p. 283). Lorenzi also notes that while we have created a leadership cult, "less has been written about the leader's specific aspirations, the social value of these aspirations, and what or whose results matter most" (p. 282). Rooke and Torbert's addition to the leadership literature begins with the statement that "leaders are made, not born, and how they develop is critical for effective organizational change" (2005, p.67). A signifi-

> In *Principled Leadership,* the leaders' pursuit of the common good is reflected in the overarching vision of helping more people recover from serious mental illnesses.

cant finding from their research is that leaders can change and evolve. Therefore, being one type of leader in a certain time and place does not necessarily translate for life, since leaders can evolve to adopt new styles (Rooke & Torbert, 2005). Working with mentors who are expert in higher level domains and learning to be exceptionally self-reflective are two of the strategies that appear to inform and facilitate individual leader transformation. Rooke and Torbert conclude that the leader's "voyage of development is not an easy one" but those who are willing to do the work often are successful (p. 76). Many of the leaders interviewed for this book reflected on their own evolution as leaders, including their own self-development.

Van Mart (2003) reviewed the mainstream literature on leadership, compared it to the public sector leadership literature and found that the latter literature pales in comparison to the former in number, scope, breadth, and research activities. Part of the difficulty in expanding the base of knowledge about effective leadership in the public sector is the complexity of the task with regard to leadership types, settings, organizational structures, frame of reference, and the difficulties in developing rigorous study methodologies. The public sector leadership literature has been even more affected by these technical difficulties, including the added burden of researching leadership behaviors in the public eye while serving the public trust (Van Mart, 2003).

> Clearly missing in *Principled Leadership,* and indeed much of the current leadership literature, is the formerly popular command and control type of leadership behavior.

Clearly missing in *Principled Leadership,* and indeed much of the current leadership literature, is the formerly popular command and control type of leadership behavior. Bennis, writing in 1999, takes a provocative swipe at such top-down leadership theories. He believes that top-down leadership is based on the idealized American myth of the triumphant hero who is seen as single-handedly, "...shattering obstacles with silver bullets and leaping tall buildings in a single bound" (p. 72). He calls this view of leadership a fantasy and that it is not the way real organizational change occurs (Bennis, 1999). Bennis states that the continuing belief in the "Great Man" theory of leadership is even more surprising, given the fact that complicated and sophisticated organizational system change requires the "coordinated contributions of many talented people working together" (p. 72). Bennis adds support to the leadership literature that focuses on the role of staff, concluding that change does not occur without willing workers. He suggests four leadership competencies that will determine success. These competencies include that the leader understands and practices the power of appreciation to its fullest extent; consistently keeps reminding people of what is important; generates and sustains trust, and is an intimate ally with followers (pp. 75–79). Bennis' words and competencies certainly find expression in the principles and tasks of the principled leaders interviewed for this book.

In concluding this overview of some of the current leadership literature, we must mention that we were particularly impressed by two books on organizational effectiveness that have direct relevance to principled leadership (Collins, 2001; Senge, 2006). Senge writes on the "learning organization," and its leaders who "come to a shared appreciation of the power of holding a vision and concurrently looking deeply and honestly at current reality" (p. 340). Collins has researched and written on why some companies develop from good to great, and has more recently extended this line of reasoning into organizations in the social sector (Collins, 2005).

> Exceptional leaders "are ambitious first and foremost for the cause, the organization, the work—not themselves—and they have the fierce resolve to do whatever it takes to make good on that ambition."
> (Collins, 2005, p.34)

Collins found that exceptional leaders "are ambitious first and foremost for the cause, the organization, the work—not themselves—and they have the fierce resolve to do whatever it takes to make good on that ambition." Collins writes that such a leader "displays a paradoxical blend of personal humility and professional will." (p. 34). We believe that the principles and tasks reported in *Principled Leadership* are germane to the masterful work on organizational effectiveness described by both Senge and Collins.

AN OVERVIEW OF THE
MENTAL HEALTH LEADERSHIP LITERATURE

Not surprisingly, a review of the literature on leadership in the mental health system yielded few significant studies. This was not unexpected, as the paucity of work in this area was one of the factors that stimulated the writing of *Principled Leadership*. James Reinertsen (2003), a physician and a health care consultant, described a blueprint for health system change, including mental health systems, that is based on his work with thirteen healthcare organizations, the Institute of Medicine (IOM) report (2001), Edward Deming's quality improvement principles (2000), and Reinertsen's own personal experience. This work centers on the importance of leadership in an organizational change process (Reinertsen, 2003).

Reinertsen states that the "central work of leadership is to bring about needed change" (2003, p. 4). He describes six leadership challenges to transforming systems that are, in fact, very consistent with the principles and tasks stressed in *Principled Leadership*. These challenges include reframing core values, creating improvement capability, collaborating across competitive boundaries, creating a business environment that assures organizational and community benefits, driving system-level rather than project-level results, and maintaining constancy of purpose over the long term (Reinertsen, 2003).

During the writing of this book on principled leadership, one of us (KH) analyzed mental health leadership by reviewing numerous efforts she has made during her career in driving mental health culture change (Huckshorn, 2005). These efforts have included integrating people in recovery from serious mental conditions into service settings as peer colleagues; developing workforce training programs for direct care staff; transitioning a county-based acute care mental health system to a sustainable model that utilized accredited and full-service general community hospitals, and creating violence-free and coercion-free mental health treatment settings. Kevin posited that the quality of leadership was the most important component in organizational culture change, and that people can learn to lead through the development of core competencies, the effective use of formal power and strong intrinsic motivation. In examining these various experiences, Kevin identified six fundamental principles of leadership that were very similar to many of the principles and tasks emphasized in *Principled Leadership*. These basic principles include the identification of a vision and core values that guide practice; the ability to motivate staff; the creation of an organizational culture that expects and then demands changes in staff behaviors; a thorough knowledge of financing and monetary incentives to change; the thoughtful and methodological use of data to measure progress, and the use of exemplary performers, including self, as drivers in the change process.

> While the current thinking about leadership seems compatible with the direction of *Principled Leadership,* the existing literature does not appear sufficient or generalizeable, in and of itself, to provide the specific model, guidance, or direction that the public mental health system will require to successfully transform itself.

In summary, the overview of the current leadership literature, including the mental health leadership literature, points to the usefulness of the principles, tasks, and examples highlighted in *Principled Leadership*. While the current thinking about leadership seems compatible with the direction of *Principled Leadership,* the existing literature does not appear sufficient or generalizeable, in and of itself, to provide the specific model, guidance, or direction that the public mental health system will require to successfully transform itself. For one's own development as a leader and as a person, we remain convinced that an effective way to learn leadership is to examine and reflect on the principles and tasks of the principled leaders that are highlighted in this book.

A FINAL WORD ON THE CONTEXT OF LEADERSHIP

Den Hartog and Koopman (2001) concluded that certain situational or contextual variables can affect, cause substitution, neutralize, or enhance the effects of leader behavior (p. 171). They identified important situational variables, including "subordinate characteristics, task characteristics, feedback, and organizational characteristics," as they make the point that effective leaders' actions often are based on the situations in which they find themselves (p. 171). Another contextual variable suggested in the literature is the extent to which the employees wish or need to have their activities directed in new ways (de Vries, Roe & Taillieu, 1998). Sounding a similar theme, Shamir & Howell (1999) believe that leadership style appears to be linked to organizational setting. They believe the relationship between leader and setting is symbiotic, in that while the leader obviously affects the setting, the setting is able to stimulate the emergence of a leadership style (Shamir & Howell, 1999).

When Linda Rosenberg was interviewed she raised this issue, as did other interviewees, about the context of leadership.

> I think the thing about effective leadership for me is that it happens in a context. You can be an expert at leadership theory and you could probably even teach it, but leadership also has to do with a time and a place. So someone could be a great leader in certain situations and not in others, probably because you need different skills. So you take someone like a Rudy Giuliani who was a great leader after 9/11; but he wasn't always such a great leader at other times. But his personality and his natural talents were a fit for a crisis. So I think you can be a great leader sometimes, but your skill set won't work in another situation. You've got to be able to live with that and know that that's okay.

Based on the leadership interviews conducted for this book, we believe Linda's comments about the context of leadership have value. Certain times and certain places cry out for leadership. Accordingly, we believe that now is the time and the mental health field is the place for principled leadership to emerge. In conclusion, we return to the premise on which this book is based, and on which we first commented in its early pages. We started with the belief that anyone can and might become a leader in mental health. The context, while important, is not as critical as what the leader brings to the context. Mental health leaders and followers probably will also be leaders in other contextual areas, e.g., social organizations, religious organizations, athletics, school organizations, etc. However, regardless of the setting or the

> We believe that now is the time and the mental health field is the place for principled leadership to emerge.

context, we believe people can become better leaders if they are guided by the principles and tasks identified in *Principled Leadership*.

Our experience in authoring this book cannot deny that ultimately leadership remains an art as well as a science. Some of the tools of leadership are not simply the tools of an expanding science of leadership. They remain the tools of the self.

1. Leaders communicate a shared vision.

- The leader makes sure the vision is a shared vision.

- The leader constantly communicates the vision.

- The leader clearly communicates the vision.

- The leader uses the vision to inspire the staff.

- The leader identifies the relevance of the vision to the organization's consumers.

- The leader lives a life compatible with the vision.

- The leader is able to persuade others of the potency of the vision.

- The leader uses the vision to shape the future.

2. Leaders centralize by mission and decentralize by operations.

- The leader uses the mission to focus the entire organization on how the organization can benefit its consumers.

- The leader identifies the separate processes that need operational leadership.

- The leader gives responsibility and authority to the operational staff.

- The leader encourages staff to process relevant information themselves.

- The leader encourages staff to participate in the decision making.

- The leader manages at a more macro than micro level.

- The leaders at the mission level serve as role models for leaders at the operational level.

- The leader identifies the different outcomes of the different units of the organization.

- The leader discerns what is required and takes those actions that are sufficient and feasible for the success of the organization.

- The leader ensures that staff understand that all operational outcomes are critical to the organization's mission.

- The leader understands that all procedures, no matter how small, reflect on the mission.

- The leader encourages communication between different levels of the organizational chart.

3. **Leaders create an organizational culture that identifies and tries to live by key values.**

- The leader is clear about what values influence organizational decision making.

- The leader uses the organization's values as anchors and guidelines for decisions.

- The leader analyzes operations by how the operations affect the organization's values.

- The leader acknowledges when organizational values conflict.

- The leader's words and behavior are congruent.

- The leader's strategies for achieving the mission are consistent with the organization's values.

- The leader's behavior in the organization reflects the organization's values.

- The leader ensures that the organization's values are the same for everyone in the organization regardless of role.

4. **Leaders create an organizational structure and culture that empowers their employees and themselves.**

- The leader sees staff as investments and assets rather than simply costs.

- The leader delegates power and authority to the employees.

- The leader ensures the staff have access to the information they need.

- The leader models how to process information.

- The leader encourages employees to think about their jobs and not just do the job.

- The leader recognizes staff who act in a empowered way.

- The leader encourages staff to develop their own opportunities—to stretch their abilities and to risk.

- The leader eliminates organizational traditions that hinder empowerment.

- The leader encourages staff to work smarter—not just harder.

- The leader recognizes employees for their outside-of-work activities.

- Leaders choose and retain staff who embody the organization's values.

- Leaders take time to reflect on their own leadership.

- Leaders access mentors who provide the leader with honest feedback, unique perspectives, and new information.

5. **Leaders ensure that staff are trained in a human technology that can translate vision into reality.**

- The leader creates an organizational culture that recognizes the value of a human technology.

- The leader understands the distinction between exposing staff to knowledge and having staff become expert in using the knowledge.

- The leader believes that staff training must focus on skills as well as facts and concepts.

- The leader emphasizes staff expertise as more critical than credentials and roles.

- The leader ensures that the organization's training plan and supervision are linked to the organization's mission.

- The leader ensures that staff are trained to think for themselves and relate skillfully with one another.

- The leader knows that trained staff have less worry about job security.

6. **Leaders relate constructively to employees.**

- The leader publicly recognizes staff contributions to the organization.

- The leader listens and expresses interest in what all levels of employees are doing.

- The leader engenders trust in the staff.

- The leader demonstrates understanding of the staff's perspectives.

- The leader models interpersonal relationships that are characterized by dignity and respect.

- The leader "thinks out loud" with staff.

- The leader knows that "front end" listening yields better outcomes.

- The leader coaches staff by first getting their perspective before giving the leader's perspective.

7. **Leaders access and use information to make change a constant ingredient of their organization.**

- The leader uses information to frame problems in new and unique ways.

- The leader sees information as the organization's capital.

- The leader uses information to create new meaning for the organization.

- The leader uses information to anticipate the future.

- The leader looks for opportunities to "stay in touch" with the environment.

- The leader thrives on change.

- The leader initiates change rather than manages change.

- The leader recognizes that maintaining the status quo is actually moving the organization backwards.

- The leader recognizes that when you are doing things well, it is time to make them better.

- The leader discriminates when consensus is and is not necessary in order for change to occur.

- The leader can still ensure involvement and participation without always achieving consensus prior to a change.

- The leader recognizes that a clear vision and values facilitate consensus to change.

- The leader knows that while planning for change is good, allegiance to plans may not always be appropriate.

- The leader realizes that changing information can change carefully constructed plans.

8. **Leaders build their organization around exemplary performers.**

- The leader directly exposes others to exemplars to maximize staff learning.

- The leader frees exemplars from organizational constraints so that exemplars can do what they do best.

- The leader recognizes that exemplars' initiative can be better modeled then taught didactically.

- The leader ensures exemplars have the organizational support they need.

- The leader understands that exemplars create opportunities for the entire organization.

- The leader leads rather than manages exemplars.

- The leader does not second guess the failures of exemplars.

- The leader understands that exemplars are strongly motivated by intrinsic rewards.

- The leader publicly recognizes the outstanding contributions of exemplars to the organization.

APPENDIX B: REQUEST FOR AN INTERVIEW

We are writing to you as someone who has been nominated as a recognized leader in the field of mental health. Due to the growing focus on what is and is not working, and the need to transform our systems of care, there has been a growing interest in what makes mental health system leaders effective. Leadership effectiveness, in this context, is defined as creating significant change in organizational and individual practice in one's respective settings toward a consumer-centered, non-coercive, and accountable system of care that leads to recovery for our service users. We are focused primarily on the identification of core principles and competencies that define effective leaders. In contrast to the world of business, there has been almost no research done in our field on this topic. Once identified, these principles and competencies can be researched and published, making effective leadership less of a magical phenomenon and more of a learned behavior.

We are authoring a textbook and workbook on this subject and would very much like to include your experiences and comments in this work. We would like to know if you would be willing to tell us about your leadership, particularly with respect to various principles and related competencies. This can be done either on the phone or through email. Specifically, we would like to use your work as a real life example of effective leadership, as we believe that this would do much to make this work come alive for readers and current and prospective leaders.

Your participation in this activity will possibly take 1–2 hours. We will ask you to describe examples of your leadership as they pertain to certain principles. Memorializing this kind of effective leadership activity is exactly what the field needs at this time. Our publisher will be the press at Boston University's Center for Psychiatric Rehabilitation. As is the regular practice of the Center, all proceeds from any published work will go to further the work of the Center and the field; no royalties will be given to the authors or others.

We have attached the Eight Principles of Leadership and their related competencies that have emerged from our already completed pilot activities. This previous work involved reviewing the leadership literature in business, and asking a number of mental health leaders to discuss their own mental health leadership with respect to certain principles. This pilot effort resulted in a significantly revised list of Eight Principles and related competences that are most relevant to mental health leadership.

Your task is to choose several of these principles and describe examples of the implementation of these leadership principles in your own setting. (Or perhaps you might suggest entirely new principles with your leadership examples.)

We have attached also a Leader Response Form so that you may complete the task online and submit it to us directly. Should you wish to do the task by phone, or not at all, please indicate your wish by replying to this email. Thanks very much for considering your participation in this project.

Sincerely,

William Anthony, PhD
Professor & Director
Center for Psychiatric Rehabilitation

Kevin Huckshorn, RN, MSN, CAP
Director of Office of Technical Assistance
NASMHPD

APPENDIX B: LEADER RESPONSE FORM

Name _____

Position title _____

Organization _____

(If position and/or organization was different for the leadership examples which follow please so indicate in the space for your examples.)

Principle No. _____:

Provide an example of how your actions illustrated this principle in a real situation at your organization. Please be as specific as possible.

Principle No. _____:

Provide an example of how your actions illustrated this principle in a real situation at your organization. Please be as specific as possible.

Do you wish to provide any other comments or additional principles? If so please use whatever space is needed.

REFERENCES

American Psychiatric Association. (1987). *Domestic and statistical manual for mental health disorders (Vol. 3).* Washington, DC: American Psychiatric Association.

American Psychiatric Association. (2000). *Diagnostic and Statistical Manual of Mental Disorders: Text Revision (4th ed.).* Washington, DC: American Psychiatric Association.

Anonymous. (1989). How I've managed chronic mental illness. *Schizophrenia Bulletin, 15,* 635–640.

Anthony, W. A. (1979). *The principles of psychiatric rehabilitation.* Baltimore: University Park Press.

Anthony, W. A. (1993a). Programs that work: Issues of leadership. *The Journal, 4*(2), 51–53.

Anthony, W. A. (1993b). Recovery from mental illness: The guiding vision of the mental health service system in the 1990's. *Psychosocial Rehabilitation Journal, 16*(4), 11–23.

Anthony, W. A. (1996a). Managed care case management for people with serious mental illness. *Behavioral Healthcare Tomorrow,* 67–69.

Anthony, W. A. (1996b). We're baaack! Community support program reemerges in a managed care context. *NAMI Advocate, 17,* 4.

Anthony, W. A. (2000). A recovery oriented service system: Setting some system level standards. *Psychiatric Rehabilitation Journal, 24*(2), 159–168.

Anthony, W. A. (2003). Expanding the evidence base in an era of recovery (editorial). *Psychiatric Rehabilitation Journal, 27*(1), 1–2.

Anthony, W. A. (2004). Overcoming obstacles to a recovery-oriented system: The necessity for state level leadership (pp. 3–7): *NASMPD Networks.*

Anthony, W. A., Brown, M. A., Rogers, E. S., & Derringer, S. (1999). A supported living/supported employment program for reducing the number of people in institutions. *Psychiatric Rehabilitation Journal, 23*(1), 57–61.

Anthony, W. A., Cohen, M. R., & Farkas, M. D. (1990). *Psychiatric rehabilitation.* Boston: Boston University, Center for Psychiatric Rehabilitation.

Anthony, W. A., Cohen, M. R., Farkas, M. D., & Gagne, C. (2002). *Psychiatric rehabilitation (2nd ed.).* Boston: Boston University, Center for Psychiatric Rehabilitation.

Ashcraft, L., & Anthony, W. A. (2005). It starts with vision. *Behavioral Healthcare Tomorrow, 14*(5), 9–11.

Bachrach, L. L. (1976). *Deinstitutionalization: An analytical review and sociological perspective.* Rockville, MD: National Institute of Mental Health.

Bass, B. M. (1990). *Bass and Stogdill's handbook of leadership: Theory, research and managerial applications.* New York: Free Press.

Beale, V., & Lambric, T. (1995). *The recovery concept: Implementation in the mental health system* (Report by the Community Support Program Advisory Committee). Columbus, OH: Ohio Department of Mental Health.

Beard, J. H., Propst, R. N., & Malamud, T. J. (1982). The Fountain House model of psychiatric rehabilitation. *Psychosocial Rehabilitation Journal, 5*(1), 47–53.

Beard, M. L. (1983). In tribute to John H. Beard. *Psychosocial Rehabilitation Journal, 6*(4), 4–6.

Beard, M. L. (1992). Social networks. *Psychosocial Rehabilitation Journal, 16*(2), 111–116.

Bennis, W. G. (1989). *On becoming a leader.* Reading, MA: Perseus Books.

Bennis, W. G. (1999). The end of leadership: Exemplary leadership is impossible without full inclusion, initiatives, and cooperation of followers. *Organizational Dynamics, 28,* 71–80.

Bennis, W. G., & Nanus, B. (1985). *Leaders: The strategies for taking charge.* New York: Harper & Rowe.

Bleuler, M. (1972). *Die schizophrenen Geistesstorungen im Lichte langjahriger Kranken und Familiengeschichten.* In Stuttgart: Georg Thieme. Translated by S.M. Clemens as *The Schizophrenic Disorders: Long-term patient and family studies.* New Haven, CT: Yale University Press, 1972.

Bolman, L. G., & Deal, T. E. (1995). *Leading with soul.* San Francisco: Jossey-Bass.

Bond, G. R., Becker, D. R., Drake, R. E., Rapp, C. A., Meisler, N., Lehman, A. F., et al. (2001). Implementing supported employment as an evidence-based practice. *Psychiatric Services, 52*(3), 313–322.

Braslow, J. T. (1995). Effect of therapeutic innovation on perception of disease and the doctor-patient relationship: A history of general paralysis of the insane and malaria fever therapy. *American Journal of Psychiatry, 152,* 660–665.

Braslow, J. T. (1997). *Mental ills and bodily cures: Psychiatric treatment in the first half of the twentieth century.* Berkeley, CA: University of California Press.

Brown, M. A., & Basel, D. (1989). A five-stage vocational rehabilitation program: Laurel Hill Center, Eugene, Oregon. In M. D. Farkas & W. A. Anthony (Eds.), *Psychiatric rehabilitation programs: Putting theory into practice* (pp. 108–116). Baltimore: Johns Hopkins University Press.

Brown, M. A., Ridgway, P., Anthony, W. A., & Rogers, E. S. (1991). Comparison of outcomes for clients seeking and assigned to supported housing services. *Hospital and Community Psychiatry, 42*(11), 1150–1153.

Brown, M. A., & Wheeler, T. (1990). Supported housing for the most disabled: Suggestions for providers. *Psychosocial Rehabilitation Journal, 13*(4), 59–68.

Burns, J. M. (1978). *Leadership.* New York: Harper and Row.

Canady, V. (2005). *SAMHSA focuses on behavioral workforce development, Special Report on Behavioral Healthcare Workforce.* Providence: Manisses Communications Group, Inc.

Carkhuff, R. R. (1971). *The development of human resources: Education, psychology and social change.* New York: Holt, Rinehart and Winston.

Carkhuff, R. R., & Benoit, D. M. (2005). *The new 3Rs: Possibilities thinking and individual freedom.* Amherst, MA: Possibilities Publishing.

Carkhuff, R. R., & Berenson, B. G. (1976). *Teaching as treatment: An instruction to counseling and psychotherapy.* Amherst, MA: Human Resource Development Press.

Carkhuff, R. R., & Berenson, B. G. (2000a). *The possibilities leader.* Amherst, MA: HRD Press.

Carkhuff, R. R., & Berenson, B. G. (2000b). *The possibilities organization.* Amherst, MA: HRD Press.

Chamberlin, J. (1978). *On our own: Patient-controlled alternatives to the mental system.* New York: Hawthorn Books.

Ciompi, L., & Müller, C. (1976). *Lebensweg und Alter der Schizophrenen: Eine katamnestische Longzeitstudie bis ins senium.* Berlin: Springer-Verlag.

Cohen, M. R. (1989). Integrating psychiatric rehabilitation into mental health systems. In M. Farkas & W. A. Anthony (Eds.), *Psychiatric rehabilitation programs: Putting theory into practice.* The Johns Hopkins series in contemporary medicine and public health (pp. 162–191). Baltimore: The Johns Hopkins University Press.

Cohen, M. R., Cohen, B., Nemec, P., Farkas, M. D., & Forbess, R. (1988). *Training technology: Case management.* Boston: Boston University, Center for Psychiatric Rehabilitation.

Collins, J. (2001). *Good to Great.* New York: Harper Collins.

Collins, J. (2005). *Good to great and the social sectors.* New York: www.jimcollins.com.

Conger, J. A. (1999). Charismatic and transformational leadership in organizations: An insider's perspective on these developing streams of research. *Leadership Quarterly, 10,* 145–170.

Connors, K. A., Graham, R. S., & Pulso, R. (1987). Playing store: Where is the vocational in psychiatric rehabilitation. *Psychosocial Rehabilitation Journal, 10*(3), 21–33.

Cook, J., & Razzano, L. (2000). Vocational rehabilitation for persons with schizophrenia: Recent research and implications for practice. *Schizophrenia Bulletin, 26*(1), 87–103.

Coyle, J., & Williams, B. (2001). Valuing people as individuals: Development of an instrument through a survey of person-centeredness in secondary care. *Journal of Advanced Nursing, 36*, 450–459.

Curie, C. G. (2005). Making life in the community for everyone a reality for America: The Substance Abuse and Mental Health Services Administration. In *Executive Forecast: Strategic Analysis of 2005 Trends* (pp. 12–13). Providence: Manisses Communication.

Deegan, P. E. (1988). Recovery: The lived experience of persons as they accept and overcome the challenge of the disability. *The Journal of the California Alliance for the Mentally Ill, 11*, 11–19.

del Vecchio, P., & Fricks, L. (2007). Guest editorial. *Psychiatric Rehabilitation Journal, 31*(1), 7–8.

Deming, W. E. (2000). *The new economics for industry, government, and politics, Second edition.* Cambridge, MA: MIT Press.

Den Hartog, D. N., & Koopman, P. L. (2001). Leadership in organizations. *Handbook of industrial, work and organizational psychology, 2*, 166–187.

DeSisto, M. J., Harding, C. M., McCormick, R. V., Ashikaga, T., & Brooks, G. W. (1995a). The Maine and Vermont three-decade studies of serious mental illness: I. Matched comparisons of cross-sectional outcome. *British Journal of Psychiatry, 167*, 331–338.

DeSisto, M. J., Harding, C. M., McCormick, R. V., Ashikaga, T., & Brooks, G. W. (1995b). The Maine and Vermont three-decade studies of serious mental illness: II. Longitudinal course comparisons. *British Journal of Psychiatry, 167* (338–341).

de Vries, R. E., Roe, R. A., & Taillieu, T. C. B. (1998). On charisma and need for leadership. *European Journal of Work and Organizational Psychology, 8*, 108–127.

Drake, R. E., McHugo, G. J., Bebout, R. R., Becker, D. R., Harris, M., Bond, G. R., et al. (1999). A randomized clinical trial of supported employment for inner-city patients with severe mental disorders. *Archives of General Psychiatry, 56*(7), 627–633.

Drake, R. E., McHugo, G. J., Becker, D. R., Anthony, W. A., & Clark, R. E. (1996). The New Hampshire study of supported employment for people with severe mental illness. *Journal of Consulting and Clinical Psychology, 64*(2), 391–399.

Drucker, P. F. (1996). Foreward: Not enough generals were killed. In F. Hesselbein, M. Goldsmith & R. Berkland (Eds.), *The leader of the future* (pp. xi–xv). San Francisco: Jossey-Bass.

Farkas, M. D., & Anthony, W. A. (2007). Bridging science to service: Using the rehabilitation research and training center program to ensure that research-based knowledge makes a difference. *Journal of Rehabilitation Research and Development, 44*(6), 879–892.

Farkas, M. D., Jette, A., Tennstedt, S., Haley, S., & Quinn, V. (2003). Knowledge dissemination and utilization in gerontology: An organizing framework. *The Gerontologist, 43*(1), 47–56.

Gardner, H. (1995). *Leading minds: An anatomy of leadership.* New York: Basic Books, Inc.

Graham, R. S. (1982). Employees support systems in a psychosocial rehabilitation setting. *Psychosocial Rehabilitation Journal, 6*(1), 12–19.

Grob, G. N. (1994a). *The mad among us: A history of the care of America's mentally ill.* New York: Maxwell Macmillan International.

Grob, G. N. (1994b). Mad, homeless, and unwanted: A history of the care of the chronic mentally ill in America. *Psychiatric Clinics of North America, 17*, 541–558.

Grob, G. N. (1996). The severely and chronically mentally ill in America: A historical perspective. In S. M. Soreff (Ed.), *Handbook for the treatment of the seriously mentally ill.* Ashland, OH: Hogrefe & Huber Publishers.

Grob, S. (1983). Psychosocial rehabilitation centers: Old wine in a new bottle. In I. Barof-sky & R. D. Budson (Eds.), *The chronic psychiatric patient in the community: Principles of treatment* (pp. 265–280). Jamaica, NY: Spectrum Publications.

Hammer, M., & Champy, J. (1993). *Reengineering the corporation: A manifesto for business revolution.* New York: Harper Collins.

Handy, C. (1996). The new language of organizing and its implications for leaders. In F. Hesselbein, M. Goldsmith & R. Berkhard (Eds.), *The leader of the future* (pp. 3–9). San Francisco: Jossey-Bass.

Harding, C. M. (1994). An examination of the complexities in the measurement of recovery in severe psychiatric disorders. In R. J. Ancill, D. Holliday & G. W. MacEwan (Eds.), *Schizophrenia: Exploring the spectrum of psychosis* (pp. 153–169). Chichester: J. Wiley & Sons.

Harding, C. M. (2003). Changes in schizophrenia across time: Paradoxes, patterns, and predictors. In C. Cohen (Ed.), *Schizophrenia into later life* (pp. 19–41). Washington, DC: APA Press.

Harding, C. M., Brooks, G. W., Ashikaga, T., Strauss, J. S., & Breier, A. (1987a). The Vermont longitudinal study of persons with severe mental illness: I. Methodology, study sample, and overall status 32 years later. *American Journal of Psychiatry, 144*(6), 718–726.

Harding, C. M., Brooks, G. W., Ashikaga, T., Strauss, J. S., & Breier, A. (1987b). The Vermont longitudinal study of persons with severe mental illness: II. Long-term outcome of subjects who retrospectively met DSM-III criteria for schizophrenia. *American Journal of Psychiatry, 144*(6), 727–735.

Harrison, G., Hopper, K., Craig, T., Laska, E., & Siegel, C. (2001). Recovery from psychotic illness: A 15–and 25–year international follow-up study. *British Journal of Psychiatry, 178,* 506–517.

Hinshaw, S. P., & Cicchetti, D. (2000). Stigma and mental disorder: Conceptions of illness, public attitudes, personal disclosure and social policy. *Development and Psychopathology, 12,* 555–598.

Hinterhuber, H. (1973). Zur Katamnese der Schizophrenien. *Fortschritte der Neurologie Psychiatrie, 41,* 527–588.

Houghton, J. F. (1982). Maintaining mental health in a turbulent world. *Schizophrenia Bulletin, 8,* 548–552.

Huber, G., Gross, G., & Schuttler, R. (1979). Schizophrenie: Verlaufs und sozialpsychiatrische Langzeit unter suchugen an den 1945 bis 1959 in Bonn hospitalisierten schizophrenen Kranken. *Monographien aus dem Gesamtgebiete der Psychiatrie Bd. 21* Berlin: Springer-Verlag.

Huckshorn, K. A. (2001). *Personal communication and observations on culture changes at South Florida State Hospital.* Unpublished papers.

Huckshorn, K. A. (2004). Reducing the use of seclusion and restraint in mental health settings: A public health approach with interventions. *Journal of Psychosocial Nursing and Mental Health Services, 42,* 22–31.

Huckshorn, K. A. (2005). *Transforming the public mental health system of care: The role of leadership in creating sustainable culture change.* Unpublished manuscript. Minneapolis: Capella University.

Huckshorn, K. A. (2007). Training the mental direct care workforce: Core constructs and competencies in a transformed system of care. *Journal of Psychosocial Nursing and Mental Health Services, 45,* 25–34.

Institute of Medicine. (2001). *Crossing the quality chasm: A new health systems for the 21st century.* Washington, DC: National Academies Press.

Institute of Medicine. (2005). *Improving the quality of health care for mental and substance abuse conditions: Quality chasm series.* Washington, DC: Academies Press.

Jacobson, N., & Curtis, L. (2000). Recovery as policy in mental health services: Strategies emerging from the states. *Psychiatric Rehabilitation Journal, 23*(4), 333–341.

Judge, T. A., & Piccolo, R. F. (2004). Transformational and transactional leadership: A meta-analytic test of their relative validity. *Journal of Applied Psychology, 89,* 755–768.

Kouzes, J. M., & Posner, B. A. (1987). *The leadership challenge: How to keep getting extraordinary things done in organizations.* San Francisco: Jossey-Bass Inc., Publishers.

Kouzes, J. M., & Posner, B. A. (1993). *Credibility: How leaders gain and lose it, why people demand it.* San Francisco: Jossey-Bass Inc. Publishers.

Kouzes, J. M., & Posner, B. A. (1995). *The leadership challenge: How to keep getting extraordinary things done in organizations (2nd ed.).* San Francisco: Jossey-Bass Inc. Publishers.

Kouzes, J. M., & Posner, B. A. (2002). *The leadership challenge (3rd ed.).* San Francisco: Jossey-Bass Inc. Publishers.

Kramer, P., Anthony, W. A., Rogers, E. S., & Kennard, W. A. (2003). Another way of avoiding the "single model trap." *Psychiatric Rehabilitation Journal, 26,* 413–415.

Kreditor, D. K. (1977). Late catamnesis of recurrent schizophrenia with prolonged remissions (according to an unselected study). *Zh Nevropatol Psikiatr Im S.S. Korsakova, 77*(1), 110–113.

Lapsley, H., Nikora, L. W., & Black, R. (2002). *"Kia Mauri Tau!" Narratives of recovery from disabling mental health problems.* Wellington: Mental Health Commission.

Leete, E. (1989). How I perceive and manage my illness. *Schizophrenia Bulletin, 15*(2), 197–200.

Legislative Summer Study Committee of the State of Vermont Division of Mental Health. (1996). A position paper on recovery and psychiatric disability. Waterbury, VT: Vermont Development Disability & Mental Health Services.

Lorenzi, P. (2004). Managing for the common good: Prosocial leadership. *Organizational Dynamics, 33,* 282–291.

Marinow, A. (1974). Klinisch-statische und katamnestische Untersuchungen und chronisch Schizophrenen 1951–1960 und 1961–1970. *Archiv fur Psychiatrie und Nervenkrankheiten, 218,* 115–124.

Mazade, N. A. (2005). Concept of transformation. Alexandria, VA: National Association of State Mental Health Program Directors Research Institute, Inc.

McDermott, B. (1990). Transforming depression. *The Journal, 1*(4), 13–14.

Micale, M. S., & Porter, R. (1994). *Discovering the history of psychiatry.* New York: Oxford University Press.

Mueser, K. T., Corrigan, P. W., Hilton, D. W., Tanzman, B., & Schaub, A. (2002). Illness management and recovery: A review of the research. *Psychiatric Services, 53*(10), 1272–1284.

Nanus, B. (1992). *Visionary leadership.* San Francisco: Jossey-Bass.

National Executive Training Institutes. (2007). *Creating violence-free and coercion-free mental health treatment settings. A training manual of the prevention of violence and the use of seclusion and restraint.* Alexandria, VA: National Association for State Mental Health Program Directors/National Technical Assistance Center for State Mental Health Planning.

Ogawa, K., Miya, M., Watarai, A., Nakazawa, M., Yuasa, S., & Utena, H. (1987). A long-term follow-up study of schizophrenia in Japan—With special reference to the course of social adjustment. *British Journal of Psychiatry, 151,* 758–765.

Onken, S., Dumont, J., Ridgway, P., Dornan, D., & Ralph, R. (2002). *Mental health recovery: What helps and what hinders? A national research project for the development of recovery facilitating system performance indicators.* Alexandria, VA: National Technical Assistance Center for State Mental Health Planning, National Association of State Mental Health Program Directors.

Packard, V. (1962). *The pyramid climbers.* New York: McGraw-Hill.

Power, A. K. (2005). Achieving the promise through workforce development: A view from the Center for Mental Health Services. *Administration and Policy in Mental Health, 32*(5/6), 489–495.

President's New Freedom Commission on Mental Health. (2003). *Achieving the promise: Transforming mental health care in America. Final report.* DHHS Pub. No. SMA–03–3832 Rockville, MD.

Quinn, R. E. (1996). *Deep change: Discovering the leader within.* San Francisco: Jossey-Bass.

Ralph, R. (2000). *Review of recovery literature: A synthesis of a sample of recovery literature 2000.* Alexandria, VA: National Technical Assistance Center for State Mental Health Planning.

Reinertsen, J. L. (2003). *A theory of leadership for the transformation of health care organizations.* Unpublished papers. January 13, 2003. Alta, WY.

Rooke, D., & Torbert, W. R. (2005). Transformations of leadership. *Harvard Business Review,* April, 67–76.

Sartorius, N., Gulbinat, W., Harrison, G., Laska, E., & Siegel, C. (1996). Long-term follow up of schizophrenia in 16 countries—A description of the international study of schizophrenia conducted by the World Health Organization. *Social Psychiatry and Psychiatric Epidemiology, 31*(5), 249–258.

Senge, P. M. (2006). *The fifth discipline: The art and practice of the learning organization.* New York: Currency Doubleday.

Shamir, B., & Howell, J. M. (1999). Organizational and contextual influences on the emergence and effectiveness of charismatic leadership. *Leadership Quarterly, 10,* 257–284.

Shern, D. L., Tsemberis, S., Anthony, W. A., Lovell, A. M., Richmond, L., Felton, C. J., et al. (2000). Serving street-dwelling individuals with psychiatric disabilities: Outcomes of a psychiatric rehabilitation clinical trial. *American Journal of Public Health, 90,* 1873–1878.

Shern, D. L., Tsemberis, S., Winarski, J., Cope, N., Cohen, M. R., & Anthony, W. A. (1997). The effectiveness of psychiatric rehabilitation for persons who are street dwelling with serious disability related to mental illness. In W. R. Breakey & J. W. Thompson (Eds.), *Mentally ill and homeless: Special programs for special needs.* Amsterdam, Netherlands: Harwood Academic.

Spillane, J. P., Halverson, R., & Diamond, J. B. (2004). Towards a theory of leadership practice: A distributed perspective. *Journal of Curriculum Studies* (36), 3–34.

State of Nebraska. (1997). *Recovery: A guiding vision for consumers and providers of mental health services in Nebraska.* Omaha: Recovery Work Team.

State of Wisconsin. (1997). *Final report. Madison, WI: Department of Health and family Services, Blue Ribbon Commission on Mental Health.*

Stein, L. I. (1992). Innovating against the current. *New directions for mental health services, 56,* 5–22.

Stein, L. I., & Test, M. A. (Eds.). (1978). *Alternatives to mental hospital treatment.* New York: Plenum Press.

Stein, L. I., & Test, M. A. (1980). Alternative to mental hospital treatment: I. Conceptual model, treatment program, and clinical evaluation. *Archives of General Psychiatry, 37*(4), 392–397.

Substance Abuse and Mental Health Services Administration News. (2004). The workforce crisis: SAMHSA's response: November/December, 12 (6) 5–8.

Swartz, M. S., Perkins, D. O., Stroup, T. S., Davis, S. M., Capuano, G., Rosenheck, R. A., et al. (2007). Effects of antipsychotic medications on psychosocial functioning in patients with chronic schizophrenia: Findings from the NIMH CATIE study. *American Journal of Psychiatry, 164*(3), 428–436.

Terry, W. (1993). *Authentic leadership: Courage in action.* San Francisco: Jossey-Bass.

Thompson, K. S., Griffith, E. E., & Leaf, P. J. (1990). A historical review of the Madison model of community care. *Hospital and Community Psychiatry, 41*(6), 625–634.

Tsemberis, S., Gulcur, L. & Nakae, M. (2004). Housing first, consumer choice and harm reduction. *American Journal of Public Health, 94*(4) 651–656.

Tsuang, M. T., Woolson, R. F., & Fleming, J. A. (1979). Long-term outcome of major psychoses. 1. Schizophrenia and affective disorders compared with psychiatrically symptom free surgical conditions. *Archives of General Psychiatry, 36,* 1295–1131.

Turner, J. C., & TenHoor, W. J. (1978). The NIMH Community Support Program: Pilot approach to a needed social reform. *Schizophrenia Bulletin, 4*(3), 319–349.

Turner, J. E., & Shifren, I. (1979). Community support system: How comprehensive? In L. I. Stein (Ed.), Community support systems for the longterm patient (*New Directions for Mental Health Services, No. 2,* pp.1–14). San Francisco: Jossey-Bass.

U.S. Department of Health and Human Services. (1999). *Mental health: A report of the Surgeon General.* Rockville, MD: U.S. Department of Health and Human Services, Substance Abuse and Mental Health Services Administration, Center for Mental Health Services, National Institutes of Health, National Institute of Mental Health.

Unzicker, R. (1989). On my own: A personal journey through madness & re-emergence. *Psychosocial Rehabilitation Journal, 13*(1), 71–77.

Van Mart, M. (2003). Public sector leadership theory: An assessment. *Public Administration Review, 63,* 214–229.

Wills, G. (1994). *Certain trumpets.* New York: Simon & Schuster.